aapi nexus

Asian Americans & Pacific Islanders
Policy, Practice & Community

A journal drawn from professional schools, applied
social science scholars and practitioners with the
explicit goal of reinvigorating Asian American Studies'
traditional mission of serving communities and
generating practical research.

PUBLISHED BY THE UCLA ASIAN AMERICAN STUDIES CENTER PRESS

SUBSCRIPTION RATES
$35.00 Individual (print + online access)—1 year/2 issues
$175.00 Institution—1 year/2 issues
$13.00 Single Issues   (CA residents add 7.25% tax
                        plus $5.00 shipping/handling)

MAILINGS AND COMMUNICATIONS
Articles for publication consideration should be sent to:
*AAPI Nexus: Asian Americans & Pacific Islanders,
Policy, Practice & Community*
UCLA Asian American Studies Center
3230 Campbell Hall, Box 951546
Los Angeles, CA 90095-1546

Phone: 310-206-7738   FAX: 310-206-9844
email: nexus@aasc.ucla.edu
For subscriptions/book orders only:
310-825-2968 FAX: 310-206-9844
web site: http://www.aasc.ucla.edu/aascpress/
nexuscollection.htm

aapi nexus

Volume 14, Number 1   Spring 2016

AAPIs 2040

This special issue has been made possible through the generous support of our sponsors—the UCLA Center for Neighborhood Knowledge, Asian Pacific American Institute for Congressional Studies (APAICS), and Eli Lilly. We are indebted to our sponsors for investing in the future of the AAPI American Dream. We also thank the staff of the UCLA Center for Neighborhood Knowledge, the UCLA AAPI Nexus Journal, and APAICS.

aapi nexus Vol. 14, No. 1 (Spring 2016): v-vii

Special Dedication

In Honor of
Don T. Nakanishi (1949 – 2016)

Co-founder and Associate Editor, *AAPI Nexus Journal*

"Whether the Oklahoman all-you-can-eat Chinese buffet owner or an Asian Australian Cabinet Minister, an Issei grandparent in a World War II concentration camp, a fresh-off-the-plane Hmong refugee, a British Desi organizing in Southall, or a Korean Brazilian making a life in Sao Paolo, Don knew that our stories and experiences have the power to augment our perspectives of diversity, advance our ideals of equality, inclusion and justice, and place us in coalitions with scholars, practitioners, activists and students to do everything in our power to move our nations and the world to change. We are grateful his work lives on through the many colleagues, staff and students with whom he worked throughout his career and take comfort in knowing that when an intellectually curious student picks up a copy of AAPI Nexus and reads any of his writings that his spirit will continue to spread for generations to come."

Marsha and Thomas Nakanishi, loving wife and son

"His work influenced and contributed to the rise of Asian American participation in all levels of government and politics in the later part of the 20th century. ... He was dedicated, insightful and compassionate, and I will always remember his incredible sense of humor, despite the seriousness of the many issues we had to face. Dr. Nakanishi was a devoted mentor to his students, a stalwart champion for Asian American scholars and activists, and a loving husband and father."

Congresswoman Judy Chu, from Congressional Record

"Don combined a passionate belief in social justice and community empowerment anchored in his formative years in East L.A. with a masterful political skill as an agent of social change. He was an institutional transformer, fighting within the belly of the beast to expand Asian American Studies and Ethnic Studies within the ivory tower without compromising a commitment to the worn but so appropriate cliché 'serve the people'. He gave unwavering moral and material support to bridging the gulf between town and gown, to making knowledge accessible to all, and to giving community a voice within the academy."

Paul Ong, co-founder with Don Nakanishi of *AAPI Nexus Journal*

"I would like to honor Don's fighter-social justice spirit. An important lesson Don taught me about research is that one of the shortcomings of quantitative analysis is to seek explanations only in relation to the data that were collected via a survey. There is very little attempt made to go beyond the collected data by drawing from other sources of knowledge, such as qualitative, historical, or voices from community leaders, etc., in order to offer fuller, more nuanced explanations. Don's inclusive approach demonstrated how Asian American Studies is about theory, praxis, storytelling, community, *and* everything else in between."

Melany De La Cruz-Viesca, Managing Editor of *AAPI Nexus Journal*

"While his life was immersed in public events, what I personally treasured most were the thoughtful, private conversations I had with him. He was a gifted listener. He gave you his undivided attention. He loved learning and knowledge. But he took all those peer-reviewed articles, all those paradigm-shifting concepts, and he brought them alive and made them real in politics, in programs, and in practices for real people. Don changed society one life at a time, but he did that over and over and over again."

Lowell Chun-Hoon, co-founder with Don Nakanishi of *Amerasia*

"He challenged theoretical understandings and empirical findings in both traditional American politics and International Relations as to the Asian American community›s multi-faceted political behaviors both in domestic and transnational contexts. Don›s scholarship emphasized the nexus between the ivory tower and community-based research for which the *AAPI Nexus*, which Don helped to establish, is an embodiment of this belief. Don's legacy will continue to inspire current and future generations of scholars, practitioners, and community members who study and work in the Asian American community."

James Lai, co-editor with Don Nakanishi of *Asian American Politics: Law, Participation, and Policy*

"Though Don's scholarly contributions are substantial, he was a masterful change agent / gentle warrior—constantly mobilizing, raising awareness, nurturing movements, creating new intellectual spaces, fighting injustice, and speaking truths. Don sparked and propelled fundraising in ethnic studies, providing perpetual support for key areas of research and study. Even after retirement, Don continued to prod, provoke and encourage those of us still on watch to right wrongs and cultivate an institution that truly valued our diverse backgrounds and views. Don inspired, counseled, supported, challenged, and cared deeply. Our souls have been nourished by his extraordinary friendship."

M. Belinda Tucker, Vice Provost, UCLA Institute of American Cultures

"*A criterion by which something is evaluated — touchstone.* Don's life-long mission of achieving social justice is reflective of all his personal and professional endeavors. Don once shared with me a bit of guiding advice that has become a daily reminder in my own work. "You can't be simply a consumer of knowledge, you must also produce knowledge." In this, and the many lasting friendships he created and nurtured, Don was a singular and prescient leader in Asian American Studies. He remains our touchstone."

Tritia Toyota, Associate Adjunct Professor in UCLA Departments of Anthropology and Asian American Studies and award-winning broadcast journalist aapi nexus Vol. 14, No. 1 (Spring 2016): viii-xiv

Message from the Editors

AAPIs 2040: Our Future

Elena Ong and S. Floyd Mori

Fifty years ago, Asian Americans and Pacific Islanders (AAPIs) were barely 1 percent of America's population, but today AAPIs are 6 percent. By the year 2040, there will be thirty-seven million AAPIs, nearly double the number of AAPIs today. In 2040, three years before America is projected to reach the "majority minority" tipping point, approximately one in ten Americans will be AAPI. As the total U.S. population increases by 18 percent, Asian Americans will increase 74 percent and Native Hawaiian and other Pacific Islanders will increase 52 percent.

What do these numbers mean for AAPIs and for America's future? To answer this question, we need to look at our past, present, and future.

AAPIs owe a debt of gratitude to the civil rights movement and activists such as Martin Luther King Jr., Cesar Chavez, and countless others for their profound impact on communities of color and the larger society. It is impossible to list the all of those who contributed to the historical transformation of race relations in the United States. AAPIs both benefited from, and participated in, the social movements of this and other monumental periods. AAPI pioneers took to the street and sought relief through the courts, demonstrating extraordinary acts of collective and individual courage, emblematically represented by people such as Yick Wo who challenged the discriminatory application of the "race-neutral" laws, Queen Lili'uokalani who fought for the sovereignty rights of Native Hawaiians, Gordon Hirabayashi and Fred Korematsu who challenged the racially motivated internment of Japanese Americans, Philip Vera Cruz who set the stage for organizing farm workers, and activists such as Grace Lee Boggs and Yuri Kochiyama who organized across the color line. Their actions and sacrifices remind us of the importance of making history by engaging history.

Changing history includes changing laws to be more just and inclusive. Had it not been for momentum created by the civil rights movement, President Lyndon B. Johnson may not have had the opportunity to sign the Civil Rights Act of 1964, the Immigration and Naturalization Act of 1965, and the Voting Rights Act of 1965. Had it not been for the Immigration and Naturalization Act's anti-discrimination policies that changed the extremely low immigration quotas from Asia and the Pacific Islands, the AAPI population would not be the size that it is today. Had it not been for the Civil Rights and Voting Rights acts, AAPIs would not have the language rights protections that they have today. Had it not been for the Voting Rights Act, AAPIs would not have the same opportunities to vote for elected officials who represent their interests.

About a quarter of a century ago the UCLA Asian American Studies Center and Leadership Education for Asian Pacifics inaugurated the nation's first Asian Pacific American Public Policy Research Institute. They published "The State of Asian Pacific America: Policy Issues to the Year 2020" in 1993, the year President Bill Clinton took office. It was the first time that AAPIs took the initiative to project that far into the future and ponder what could happen with an AAPI policy agenda if the community increased from eight million Asian Pacific Americans in 1990 to twenty million Asian Pacific Americans by the year 2020.

Over the last quarter of a century, AAPIs have made great strides in America—with Secretary Norman Mineta becoming the first Asian American appointed to a presidential cabinet for two U.S. presidents; to the late U.S. Senator Daniel Inouye, who as president pro tem of the U.S. Senate was the highest-ranking Asian American politician in U.S. history; to U.S. Senator Mazie Hirono, the first Asian American woman to serve in the U.S. Senate. AAPIs were also given a voice in the White House, when President Bill Clinton established, and President George W. Bush and President Barack Obama reauthorized, the first White House Initiative on Asian American and Pacific Islanders. Now in 2016, we have the largest number of AAPIs in history to ever serve in U.S. Congress.

Today, Asian Americans and Pacific Islanders are two of the nation's fastest-growing racial populations and are already twenty million strong. History and current events have demonstrated that our presence in numbers matters.

Now the question is: "What do we envision a quarter century from today?"

To answer that question, the UCLA Center for Neighborhood Knowledge (previously the UCLA Center for the Study of Inequality), Asian Pacific American Institute for Congressional Studies (APAICS), and the UCLA *AAPI Nexus Journal* invited many of the organizations affiliated with the National Council on Asian Pacific Americans to an inaugural meeting in early 2015, to give rise to this special 2040 edition of the *AAPI Nexus Journal*.[1] We challenged AAPI community leaders to look at where we've been, where we are, and where we want to be in 2040.

Our goal was to develop our own narrative through a collection of essays that would help shape the contours of a vision for the 2040 AAPI Dream. To understand our power in 2040, we studied projections[2] that revealed that by 2040:

- There will be thirty-seven million AAPIs.
- Nearly one in ten Americans will be of AAPI descent at a time when nearly one in two Americans will be persons of color.
- One in seven voters will be of Asian American descent.
- Asian American elderly will increase 178 percent and Pacific Islander elderly will increase 205 percent while the number of elderly overall will increase 72 percent.
- One out of six Asian Americans and more than half of Pacific Islanders will be multiracial, and
- About half of Asian Americans and one out of five of Pacific Islanders will be U.S.-born.

We asked a diverse range of AAPI spokespersons[3] to speculate on what the implications of these numbers would mean for the AAPI community. We asked: "What should AAPIs do today to create and actualize a better AAPI and American future?"

Based on their written thoughts in this special issue's essays, most of the authors feel that "the fight for the future" is now. These authors feel that not enough is being done to address social inequities, and that there needs to be a combination of leadership, power, and accountability to change what is to what should be. Without intervention, some see a bleak future for Native Hawaiians and Pacific Islanders, Muslims and "other" yellow and brown peoples, and refugees. Without intervention, some see a long protracted struggle for AAPI aging, AAPI poor and near poor, AAPI women, and AAPIs who identify as LGBTQ. Some feel that AAPIs are viewed with undeserved suspicion. Many feel that AAPIs are one of the most poorly understood groups in America because aggregated data fails to dispel the myth of the successful minority. The authors share their vision for educational equity, health equity, economic justice, environmental justice, gender equity, LGBTQ equality, and political equality, but feel that there is a lack of capacity and institutional infrastructure to address the dynamically changing demographics of AAPI issues and needs.

By contrast, some of the authors feel that AAPIs are finally coming of age and that "the future is now." These authors feel that AAPIs are finally making progress, but only after significant efforts to increase participation and representation in all sectors, particularly in media, business, and philanthropy. They see a brighter future for AAPIs, provided AAPIs accept the responsibility and consequences of success by giving back to the community and lifting others up the ladder of success.

We are excited to share this collection of essays in two volumes. The first volume addresses leadership, power, equity, and justice, examining contemporary issues in the AAPI communities and what the future could look like with and without appropriate policy interventions. As nation of native-born, and a nation of immigrants, we present demographic projections of Native Hawaiian and Pacific Islander communities, and of the Asian American communities. We know that demographics are not destiny, so we begin the journal with an essay on AAPIs and the economy, and we look at our AAPI past, present and future, through a justice lens. Recognizing that the America's health and socioeconomic well-being depends on the multiple determinants of health, we include essays on the economy and economic justice, K-12 education, higher education, workforce participation, aging, health, environmental justice, and immigration. We conclude Volume I with an essay on the importance of a political trajectory for AAPIs by 2040. The second volume looks at the AAPI community through a population and a legacy lens. We begin Volume II with essays on Native Hawaiians and Pacific Islanders, the profiling of Asian Pacific Islander America, AAPI women, and the LGBTQ AAPI communities, to assess the progress that still needs to be made. We also look at the opportunity to create and sustain a legacy for the future, by looking the plight of AAPIs in business, in media, in philanthropy, in Asian American & Ethnic Studies, and in cultural and historic preservation.

AAPI 2040 provides a window to the future. It offers what AAPIs want to see for the AAPI Dream by examining it at the likely trajectory versus a desired trajectory. It also provides recommendations for how to achieve the AAPI Dream.

But what good is vision without the moral compass, people, resources, and action to turn the dream into reality?

To actualize to our 2040 vision, we need to develop the 2040 Blueprint that will chart our course for the future. To actualize our 2040 vision, we also need to invest in people and cultivate a 2040 AAPI leadership pipeline, for we will need people from the grass tops to the grass roots to navigate change from the inside out and the outside in. We also need to cultivate the resources that will shore up capacity and infrastructure.

A 2040 Blueprint for Policy and Community Action could consist of:

1. Making the collection and utilization of disaggregated data a consumer expectation, a business practice, and a governmental priority.
2. Building an AAPI leadership pipeline in business, philanthropy, government, and community that can navigate the journey to the vision in the short and long run.
3. Leveraging resources and strategic alliances for a movement that advances a pathway to equity.

You cannot change any society unless you take responsibility for it, unless you see yourself as belonging to it and responsible for changing it.

Grace Lee Boggs, 2012[4]

You are the future.

We are at the beginning of this journey. We need to take action to create a society that we want. We need to be visionary and create a trajectory that bends toward the arc of justice. We also need to recognize the challenges in the journey ahead. We need to create and advance the internal and external policy dialogue, the strategic leadership alliances, and the pipeline of policy makers and decision makers, who will strengthen our position now and for the future.

We invite you—the reader, the professional, the scholar, and the activist—to play an active role in advancing our AAPI future. This is a living document. We invite you to engage with the authors who reimagined America's future with creativity, wisdom, and inspirational leadership. We thank them and the organizations they are affiliated with. We also thank the staff of the UCLA Center for Neighborhood Knowledge, the UCLA *AAPI Nexus Journal*, and APAICS. We are also indebted to our sponsors—the UCLA Center for Neighborhood Knowledge, APAICS, and Eli Lilly—for investing in the future of the AAPI American Dream. We also acknowledge the late UCLA Professor Don Nakanishi for his inspiring words for our future.

For today, with twenty million AAPIs, America's marble ceiling is still cold and hard—we still haven't had an AAPI president of the United States or an AAPI U.S. Supreme Court Justice. In addition, the number of AAPI CEOs continues to be far and few between—far too few have shattered the glass and bamboo ceilings. Worse, without data disaggregation, many populations within the AAPI community who experience persistent health, educational, social, and income inequities will continue to be invisible, and their issues not heard, addressed, or resolved.

But by the year 2040, when roughly one in ten Americans is AAPI, the AAPI Dream will be within reach. By 2040, AAPIs will break the marble ceiling. By 2040, there will be significant AAPI presence and leadership in Congress, on commissions, and in the C-suite. By 2040, there will be resources and infrastructure to advance a pathway to equity. After all, the AAPI Dream is not just about attainment or buying power,[5] success is about equity and justice. No AAPI forgotten, or left behind.

Let's promise to continue the journey by investing time and resources in actualizing this vision over the next twenty-five years. Let's promise to convene before 2040, on the seventy-fifth anniversary of the Civil Rights Act, before America reaches the "majority minority" tipping point, to assess how well we weathered the journey and see if we actualized our vision by sustaining the strategic alliances and collaborations to reach, if not exceed, our goals.

Notes

1. The idea for the 2040 project was developed by Paul Ong. Key influencers include J.D. Hokoyama, Melany De La Cruz-Viesca, S. Floyd Mori, Elena Ong, Amy Watanabe, and the National Council of Asian Pacific Americans.

2. These projections were based on the U.S. Census 2014 National Population Projections and customized for the AAPI community by Paul, Jonathan, and Elena Ong.

3. The authors were younger and older; U.S.-born, immigrant, and/or refugee; Pacific Islander and Asian American; mono-racial, multiracial, and/or in a multiracial relationship; and women, men, as well as persons identifying as LGBTQ.

4. Grace Lee Boggs was the author of *The Next American Revolution: Sustainable Activism for the Twenty-First Century* (Oakland: University of California Press, 2012.)

5. Some believe that the AAPI Dream can be measured in buying power. If it were, AAPI buying power is projected to exceed $1.25 trillion by 2040. If AAPI America were its own separate nation, its spending power could rank among the world's top twenty economies.

ELENA ONG is the Vice President of Ong and Associates, where she is a public policy and public affairs consultant to elected officials and nonprofits. Committed to advancing America's health and economic well-being, she served as the President/CEO of the Asian and Pacific Islander Caucus for Public Health prior to being elected to APHA's Executive Board. Committed to public service, Elena has served in a leadership capacity on several U.S. presidential and gubernatorial campaigns, as the governor's appointed First Vice Chair to the California Commission for Women, as Rob Reiner's appointee to the California Children and Families Commission's TA Advisory Board, and as President of the Los Angeles Women's Appointment Collaboration. A recent CORO Executive Fellow, Elena studied Asian American studies at UC Berkeley prior to earning her BSN/PHN from UC San Francisco, and her master's in health policy and management from the Harvard School of Public Health while cross-enrolled at the Kennedy School of Government.

S. FLOYD MORI is the President and CEO of the Asian Pacific American Institute for Congressional Studies (APAICS). Previously, Mori served as the National Executive Director/CEO of the Japanese American Citizens League (JACL). He was chair of the National Coalition of Asian Pacific Americans and has been on the Executive Council of the Leadership Conference on Civil and Human Rights. He served four years as National President and four years as a National Vice President of the JACL. Mori was elected in 1972 to the city council for Pleasanton, California, where he served as Mayor ProTem and later as Mayor. He was also elected to the California State Assembly and served for six years as an Assemblyman. He has received a number of awards including an Outstanding Citizen Achievement Award from OCA, the Community Leadership Award from APAICS, and the Order of the Rising Sun, Gold Rays with Rosette Award from the Government of Japan.

aapi nexus Vol. 14, No. 1 (Spring 2016): 1-13

Resource Paper

The Future of Pacific Islander America in 2040

Paul Ong, Elena Ong, and Jonathan Ong

Abstract

This resource paper analyzes the growth of the Native Hawaiian and Other Pacific Islander (NHOPI) population over the next quarter century based on projections from the U.S. Census Bureau and supplementary estimates by the authors. Overall, this population will increase from about 1.5 million in 2015 to nearly 2.3 million in 2040, about three times greater than the increase for the total U.S. population. Most NHOPIs are indigenous, but immigrants comprise about a fifth of the population. This group is relatively young, but median age will increase over time. Youth comprised about a third of the population in 2015 and over a quarter in 2014. The elderly share will nearly double to about one in eight by 2040. NHOPIs are more likely to be multiracial than any other racial group, and NHOPIs of mixed-race will comprise over half the population a quarter century from now.

Introduction

According to the U.S. Census Bureau, the number of Native Hawaiians and Other Pacific Islanders (NHOPIs) will increase from about 1.5 million in 2015 to nearly 2.3 million in 2040, a 52 percent increase, which is three times greater than the increase for the total U.S. population (18 percent). NHOPIs (a.k.a. Pacific Islanders) will be an integral part of a profound social, cultural, political, and economic transformation as the nation becomes majority minority in 2043. In many ways, Pacific Islanders epitomize the demographic changes. It is the group with the highest proportion of individuals of mixed race, and with the highest proportion of youth. At the same time, the percent of NHOPIs that is comprised of immigrants is above the proportion for the entire nation. This report provides some insights about the historical context and characteristics

1

of the emerging Pacific Islander population, focusing on the quarter century between 2015 and 2040.

This report is also a part of a larger project that builds on the pioneering work that was published more than two decades ago, "The State of Asian Pacific America, Policy Issues to the Year 2020," jointly published in 1993 by LEAP (Leadership Education for Asian Pacifics) and UCLA's Pacific Islander Studies Center. As with that edited volume, we believe that it is critical to understand key characteristics of the future population of Pacific Islanders, particularly by nativity and age. Doing so enables us to better understand Pacific Islander concerns and priorities, gain potential insights into the nature of social relations among demographic subgroups of Pacific Islanders, and speculate on their political and economic contributions to the nation.

While others have made projections of the Pacific Islander population, this project provides details not available elsewhere (see Pew Research Center, 2012). Rather than use a simple linear extrapolation for all Pacific Islanders, collapsing Pacific Islanders with "others," or reporting only for "Pacific Islanders Alone," this project utilizes demographic projection techniques that enhance the most recent 2014 National Population Projections by the U.S. Census Bureau (2015).[1] The project also takes into account differences in racial classifications over time[2] and develops projections of the absolute and relative size of the multiracial Pacific Islanders by nativity and age (i.e., U.S.-born or native-born).[3]

The report is organized into four sections. The first section provides a brief historical background and population projections of NHOPIs who live in the fifty states and the District of Columbia. The counts and projections do not include 168,000 Pacific Islanders who live in the Pacific territories.[4] The second section examines the role of immigration, which contributes proportionately more to the growth of the NHOPI population than for the general population. Section three discusses the age distribution of Pacific Islanders, which is a much younger population relative to the general population, although the growth rate for the elderly will be very high. Section four examines multiracial NHOPIs. The report concludes with some implications.

Historical Background and Population Projections

The NHOPI population has been formed through a rich and complex history that involved colonization, disposition, and near genocide of indigenous groups, and more recently, immigration (Barringer, Gardner, and Levin, 1995; Camacho, 2011; Ong, 2006; Wright, 2002). Because it is has been a relatively small population, Pacific Islanders have been officially enumerated in recent decades.[5] The 1980 Census counted more than 259,000 Pacific Islanders by race (Barringer et al., 1995, 273).[6] A decade later, the 1990 Census reported 365,000, a 41 percent increase (U.S. Census Bureau, 1993a; U.S. Census Bureau, 1993b, 1).[7] Because the 2000 Census allowed individuals to check one or more responses to the race question, there are two official counts, 379,000 who identified as being NHOPI alone, and 861,000 who identified as being NHOPI alone or in combination with another race (the latter is also known as the inclusive count) (U.S. Census Bureau, 2005). By 2010, the alone count climbed to 540,000, and the inclusive count to 1,225,000. The 40.1 percent increase from 2000 for the inclusive count was four times greater than for the total population (9.7 percent) (U.S. Census Bureau, 2012, 4).

The NHOPI population is projected to continue to increase at a much more rapid rate than the general population (see Figure 1 for projections).[8] Between 2015 and 2040, the NHOPI inclusive population will increase by 52 percent, while the total U.S. population will increase by 18 percent.

Figure 1. NHOPIS Inclusive (x 1,000)

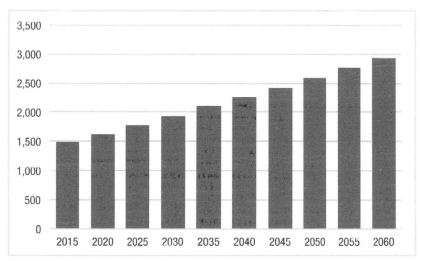

Source: Authors' analysis and compilation of U.S. Census Bureau's 2014 National Population Projections

Pacific Islanders by Nativity

Although most NHOPIs have indigenous ancestry, immigrants comprise a significant minority of this population, due in large part from the elimination of racially biased restriction on immigration in 1965.[9] Figure 2 shows the number entering from the Oceania region of the world, excluding Australia and New Zealand. While immigrants from "Other Oceania" are ethnically and racially diverse, a significant number are Pacific Islanders.[10]

Figure 2. Immigrants from "Other Oceania"

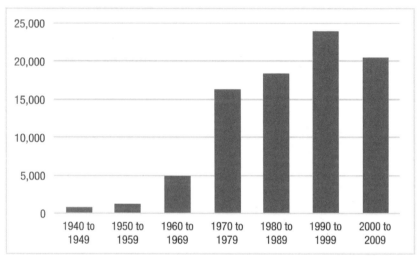

Source: Office of Immigration Statistics' 2013 Yearbook of Immigration Statistics

As a result, immigrants (foreign-born individuals) comprise a significant minority among NHOPIs. In 1980, they comprised about 11 percent (U.S. Census Bureau, 1993a, B-26).[11] That proportion increased to about 13 percent in 1990, with the majority having already entered the country in the previous decade (U.S. Census Bureau, 1993a, 25; U.S. Census Bureau, 1993b, 3).[12] By the turn of the century, nearly one in five was foreign-born, with nearly three-quarters entering since 1980 (U.S. Census Bureau, 2005, 20).[13]

The foreign-born segment also comprises roughly one in five of the inclusive Pacific Islander count in the Census Bureau's 2015 baseline for its population projections. While the absolute number of immigrants will continue to increase, their share will decrease.[14] By 2040, they will comprise 17 percent (compared to 20 percent in 2015). The relative size of the immigrant segment varies by age. Figure 3 shows composition by nativity in 2015 (first five bars) and 2040 (last five bars).

Figure 3. NHOPIs by Age and Nativity

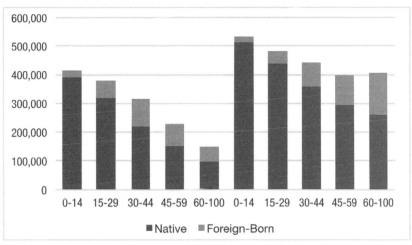

Source: Authors' analysis and compilation of U.S. Census Bureau's 2014 National Population Projections

Distribution by Age

Figure 4 depicts the distribution of the Pacific Islander population in 2015 and 2040. There is a distinctive bulge among prime working-age adults, noticeable among younger adults (twenty-five to thirty-four years old) in 2015 and extending up to age forty-four in 2040.

Figure 4. NHOPI Age Distribution

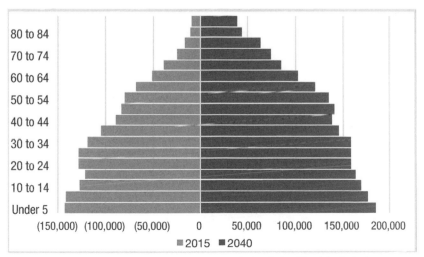

Source: Authors' analysis and compilation of U.S. Census Bureau's 2014 National Population Projections

Like the nation as a whole, the Pacific Islander population will age over time. The median age of the Pacific Islander population will increase from twenty-seven years old in 2015 to thirty-two years old in 2040.[15] While all age groups will increase in absolute numbers, there are noticeable differences in the relative share. Over the next quarter century, youth (persons seventeen and younger) will decline from 33 percent to 28 percent of all Pacific Islanders, while elderly (persons sixty-five and older) will increase from 7 percent to 13 percent. Unlike the U.S. population as a whole, there is no baby boom bulge in 2015 among NHOPIs, due to the specific demographic history of Pacific Islanders.

Despite the differential growth rates by age group among NHOPIs, this group will continue to have the highest proportion comprised of young people. Figure 5 reports the percent that is seventeen and younger for the major racial groups (inclusive count) and Hispanics. Over the next half century, that percent will decline for all racial groups and Hispanics, a product of falling fertility rate and continued immigration of adults. The percentage for Pacific Islanders will decline from 33 percent in 2015 to 28 percent in 2040, but nonetheless will be more than 2 percentage points higher than the next three groups (Hispanics, blacks, and American Indians).

Figure 5. Percent Seventeen and Younger

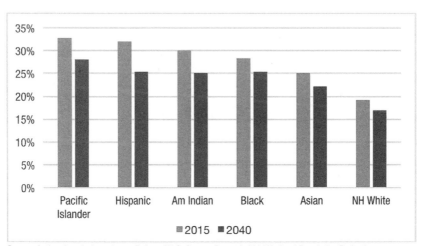

Source: Authors' analysis and compilation of U.S. Census Bureau's 2014 National Population Projections

Multiracial Pacific Islanders

Pacific Islanders have extremely high rates of out-marriage, or conversely very low rates of in-marriage. An analysis of the 2011–13 American Community Survey shows the extent. Among married couples where at least one of the partners is Pacific Islander, only 17.6 percent is comprised of couples where both partners are NHOPIs alone. More recently married (those married in 2005 or later) have a lower in-marriage rate, at 16.8 percent. Place of residents has an influence, with the rate being higher in Hawaii, at 20.3 percent. Given this pattern, it is not surprising that a high proportion of Pacific Islanders are of mixed racial heritage.

In 2015, the number of NHOPIs alone (those who reported only one race) is roughly equal to the number of NHOPIs who are multiracial (see Figure 6).[16] Moreover, a disproportionate number of Pacific Islanders are more likely to be more than multiracial. About a third of multiracial Pacific Islanders reported three or more races, while only one in twelve other mixed-race individuals reported three or more races.[17] However, there is a significant difference in the growth rates of these two segments over the next quarter century: 38 percent for Pacific Islanders alone and 66 percent for mixed-race NHOPIs. Consequently, the number of multiracial Pacific Islanders will surpass the number of NHOPIs alone. By 2040, multiracial individuals will comprise 54.5 percent of the NHOPI inclusive count.

Figure 6. NHOPI Projections by Race (x 1,000)

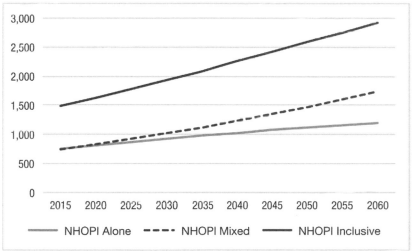

Source: Authors' analysis and compilation of U.S. Census Bureau's 2014 National Population Projections

Figure 7 shows the percent that is multiracial by age group. The projections indicate that the rates are highly age related. Among those nineteen and younger, multiracial Pacific Islanders will go from a large majority in 2015 (57 percent) to a super majority in 2040 (66 percent). The percentage point increase among adults is less dramatic because immigration will add to the alone category. The elderly segment will actually move in the opposite direction, that is, the mixed-race percent will decline.

Figure 7. Multiracial Percent of NHOPIs

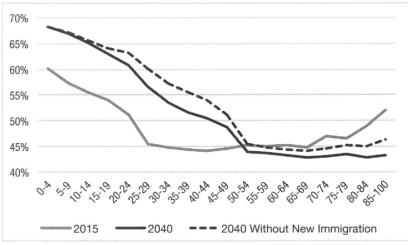

Source: Authors' analysis and compilation of U.S. Census Bureau's 2014 National Population Projections

Figure 8. Percent Multiracial

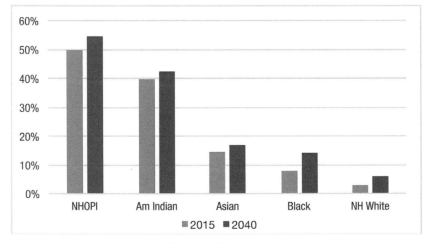

Source: Authors' analysis and compilation of U.S. Census Bureau's 2014 National Population Projections

Not only is the mixed-race rate high for NHOPIs, it is higher than for any other racial groups, as show in Figure 8. In 2015, the rate for Pacific Islanders is about 10 percentage points higher than for American Indians, another population that is predominantly indigenous.

Concluding Remarks

The United States is undergoing a dramatic demographic transformation. By 2043, America will become "majority minority" and reach a new historic social, economic, and political configuration. In many ways, Pacific Islanders have been and will continue to be a microcosm of an ever-increasingly diverse multicultural and multiracial America. The U.S. Census Bureau reported two dozen NHOPI ethnic groups from the 2010 enumeration, each with its own distinct cultural traditions, language, and relationship within the United States. The NHOPI population is further diversified because a majority will come from mixed-marriage families, as documented in the previous sections. Unfortunately, the U.S. Census does not provide detailed information on each NHOPI group, in part because of the "small number" challenge. NHOPIs constitute the smallest population among the five major racial categories covered by federal minimum reporting standards. The lack of adequate reporting, however, does a disservice because it obscures the distinct historical trajectories and contemporary conditions experienced by each NHOPI community. We believe that data disaggregation is important, but given the limited resources and information for this report, we were unable to disaggregate the NHOPI projections. The good news is that producing specialized NHOPI reports is less challenging these days because of advances in data technologies. As we move forward to 2040, we expect better reporting of this population.

Acknowledgements

We are indebted to David Armstrong and Jennifer Ortman of the U.S. Census Bureau for their technical review and expertise; and to Chhandara Pech and Silvia Jimenez at UCLA's Center for Neighborhood Knowledge for their technical assistance.

Notes

1. The U.S. Census Bureau reports projections by nativity only for Pacific Islanders alone. We supplement those projections with our own estimates for multiracial Pacific.
2. The project also accounts for the differences in the racial/ethnic categories used for the Census Bureau's population projection models and the

categories used for other Census Bureau data sources, such as the decennial census and the American Community Survey. The projections' categories are consistent with those used by the U.S. National Center for Health Statistics. For a discussion on the differences, see National Center for Health Statistics, 2015.

3. This also includes a small number who were born in the U.S. territories or abroad to American citizens. We use microlevel data from the American Community Survey to estimate the age distribution of multiracial NHOPIs by nativity. To project the number of mixed-race Pacific Islanders in 2040, we developed a crude fertility rate for mixed-raced Pacific Islander adults (whose children would also be mixed race) and an adjusted fertility rate for Pacific Islander alone adults who are likely to have mixed-race children.

4. This 2010 count covers American Samoa, Guam, and North Mariana Islands (American Fact Finder, 2010). NHOPIs comprise about 62 percent of the total population in those islands, and Asian Americans comprise 34 percent.

5. The 1960 U.S. Census questionnaire included "Hawaiian" and "Part Hawaiian" for the state of Hawaii only, and the 1970 U.S. Census included "Hawaiian" for all states except Alaska. In subsequent decades, the number of Pacific Islander categories increased. The U.S. Census reported 102,403 who were either Hawaiian and part Hawaiian residing in Hawai'i in 1960, and 100,179 Hawaiians in the United States (except Alaska) in 1970 (Gibson and Jung, 2002).

6. There were 172,346 Hawaiians, 39,520 Samoans, and 31,393 Chamorro. These counts did not include many who were of mixed race and ancestry. There were 406,413 individuals who reported being Pacific Islander by race or ancestry or both.

7. The 1980 and 1990 counts are not completely comparable because of changes in questionnaire and collection method.

8. The Census Bureau's population projection models use racial/ethnic categories that differ from those for the decennial census and the American Community Survey. The projections' categories are consistent with those used by the U.S. National Center for Health Statistics. For a discussion on the differences, see National Center for Health Statistics, 2015.

9. For details on the changes in immigration policy and laws, see Ong, Ong, and Ong, 2015.

10. Migration from U.S. territories is not included in the immigration numbers. An analysis of the 2011–13 American Community Survey microdata indicates that roughly one in twelve Pacific Islanders are from U.S. territories.

11. Based on statistics in Barringer et al. (1995, 285–6): 83,037 (out of 259,566) were born outside of the United States, including those in U.S. territories and trusts (9,361 American Samoa, 36,782 Guam, 2,137 Northern Marinas, 5,066 Trust Territories). The Census Bureau defines a native as a person born in the United States, Puerto Rico, or an outlying area of the United

States, including those born abroad to U.S. citizens. Foreign-born are those born abroad without citizenship.

12. Percentages based on data from the U.S. Bureau of the Census note that Tongans having the highest percent (61 percent) (1993b). U.S. Bureau of the Census (1993a, 25) also reported 45,397 (out of 350,592) were foreign-born, with 24,612 immigrated between 1980 and 1990.

13. There were 75,477 single-race NHOPIs where were foreign-born (20 percent of all NHOPIs alone), and 161,601 inclusive NHOPIs (18.8 percent of the inclusive count). For inclusive population, year of entry (14,470 entered before 1970, 28,515 during the 1970s, 50,040 during the 1980s, and 68,576 during the 1990s).

14. The Census Bureau assumes an annual rate of 4,000 to 5,000 net immigration for NHOPIs alone. In absolute terms, the number of Pacific Islander immigrants is projected to increase from 304,000 in 2015 to 309,000 in 2040.

15. NHOPIs have been a relatively young population. For example, "In 2000, Pacific Islanders had a median age of 28 years, compared with 35 years for the total U.S. population" (U.S. Census Bureau, 2005, 5).

16. This is certainly not a recent phenomenon. In 1960, there were 11,294 Hawaiians and 91,109 part Hawaiians residing in Hawai'i (Gibson and Jung, 2002). In 1980, 44 percent of Pacific Islanders by ancestry were of multiancestry (a combination of Pacific Islander and non–Pacific Islander ancestries) (Barringer et al., 1995, 273).

17. Estimates by authors based on 2011–13 American Community Survey microdata.

References

American Fact Finder. 2010. Demographic Profiles. http://factfinder.census.gov/faces/nav/jsf/pages/index.xhtml (accessed August 26, 2015).

Barringer, Herbert, Gardner, Robert W., and Michael J. Levin. 1995. *Asians and Pacific Islanders in the United States*. New York: Russel Sage Foundation.

Camacho, Keith. 2011. *Cultures of Commemoration: The Politics of War, Memory, and History in the Mariana Island*. Honolulu: University of Hawai'i Press.

Gibson, Campbell, and Kay Jung. 2002. "Historical Census Statistics on Population Totals by Race, 1790 to 1990, and by Hispanic Origin, 1970 to 1990, for the United States, Regions, Divisions, and States." U.S. Census Bureau, Working Paper No. 56.

National Center for Health Statistics. 2015. "U.S. Census Populations with Bridged Race Categories." Centers for Disease Control and Prevention. http://www.cdc.gov/nchs/nvss/bridged_race.htm (accessed February 17, 2016).

Ong, Jonathan, Ong, Paul, and Elena Ong. 2016. "The Future of Asian America in 2040." *AAPI Nexus Journal: Policy, Practice, and Community* 14(1): 14–29.

Ong, Paul. 2006. "Trouble in Paradise: Marginalization of Native Hawaiians." Pp. 155–72 in *Wealth Accumulation and Communities of Color in the United States*, ed. Jessica Gordon Nembhard and Ngina Chiteji. Ann Arbor: University of Michigan Press.

Pew Research Center. 2012. "The Rise of Asian Americans." Pew Research Center Social and Demographic Trends. 19 June. http://www.pewsocialtrends.org/2012/06/19/the-rise-of-asian-americans/ (accessed April 12, 2015).

U.S. Census Bureau. 2015. 2014 National Populations Projections Methodology. https://www.census.gov/population/projections/files/methodology/methodstatements14.pdf (accessed April 12, 2015).

———. 2012. "The Native Hawaiian and Other Pacific Islander Population: 2010." https://www.census.gov/prod/cen2010/briefs/c2010br-12.pdf (accessed April 12, 2015).

———. 2005. "We the People: Pacific Islanders in the United States." Census 2000 Special Reports. https://www.census.gov/prod/2005pubs/censr-26.pdf (accessed April 12, 2015).

———. 1993a. "1990 Census of Population: Asians and Pacific Islanders in the United States." https://www.census.gov/prod/cen1990/cp3/cp-3-5.pdf (accessed April 12, 2015).

———. 1993b. "We the Americans: Pacific Islanders." https://www.census.gov/prod/2005pubs/censr-26.pdf (accessed April 12, 2015).

U.S. Department of Homeland Security. Office of Immigration Statistics. 2014. "2013 Yearbook of Immigration Statistics." Washington, DC: U.S. Department of Homeland Security. https://www.dhs.gov/sites/default/files/publications/ois_yb_2013_0.pdf (accessed April 12, 2016).

Wright, Debbie Hippolite. 2002. *Pacific Diaspora: Island Peoples in the United States and across the Pacific*. Honolulu: University of Hawaii Press.

PAUL ONG is a professor at UCLA's Luskin School of Public Affairs and UCLA's Asian American Studies Department. He is currently the Director of the UCLA Center for Neighborhood Knowledge, founding editor of *AAPI Nexus: Policy, Practice and Community*, and founding director of the UC AAPI Policy Multi-Campus Research Program. He has conducted research on immigration, civic and political participation, economic status of minorities, welfare-to-work, health workers, urban spatial inequality, and environmental inequality.

ELENA ONG is the Vice President of Ong and Associates, where she is a public policy and public affairs consultant to elected officials and nonprofits. Committed to advancing America's health and economic well-being, she served as the President/CEO of the Asian and Pacific Islander Caucus for Public Health prior to being elected to APHA's Executive Board. Committed to public service, Elena has served in a leadership capacity on several U.S. presidential and gubernatorial campaigns, as the governor's appointed First Vice Chair to the California Commission for Women, as Rob Reiner's appointee to the California Children and Families Commission's TA Advisory Board, and as President of the Los Angeles Women's Appointment Collaboration. A recent CORO Executive Fellow, Elena studied Asian American studies at UC Berkeley prior to earning her BSN/PHN from UC San Francisco, and her masters in Health Policy and Management from the Harvard School of Public Health while cross-enrolled at the Kennedy School of Government.

JONATHAN ONG is a data analyst and statistical programmer. He has worked and published on the socioeconomic status of American Indians in Los Angeles, New York's Chinatown, and fair housing in California. Jonathan is a graduate of UCLA, with a major in Japanese and a minor in film, and is currently studying computer science.

aapi nexus Vol. 14, No. 1 (Spring 2016): 14-29

Resource Paper

The Future of Asian America in 2040

Jonathan Ong, Paul Ong, and Elena Ong

Abstract

This resource paper analyzes the growth of the Asian American (AA) population over the next quarter century based on projections from the U.S. Census Bureau and supplementary estimates by the authors. The number of Asian Americans will increase from 20.5 million in 2015 to 35.7 million in 2040, making them the fastest-growing racial population in the nation. Like the nation as a whole, the AA population will age over the next quarter century, with youth declining from a quarter to a little more than a fifth of the AA population and the elderly increasing from a tenth to about a sixth. Immigrants will continue to be a majority of Asian Americans, but their share will decline from two-thirds to one half. After 2040, U.S.-born AAs (those who are Asian alone and from mixed-race backgrounds) will comprise a majority of the population. Another significant change will be the growth of multiracial Asian Americans, increasing from a tenth of the population 1990 to a sixth in 2040.

Introduction

According to the U.S. Census Bureau, the number of Asian Americans will increase 74 percent, from 20.5 million in 2015 to 35.7 million in 2040, making Asian Americans the fastest-growing racial population in the nation. This demographic trajectory will have profound social, cultural, political, and economic implications when Asian Americans constitute nearly a tenth of the total U.S. population in 2040, at approximately the same time that America becomes majority minority in 2043.[1] This resource paper provides insights into the historical context and characteristics of the emerging population. Immigrants and single-race Asian Americans[2] will continue to comprise a majority of this population through most of the time period; nonetheless, there will a noticeable demographic recomposition. Two of the most important projected changes are the absolute and relative growth of U.S.-born Asian Americans and of multiracial Asians Americans. Both transformations will be concentrated among children and young adults. This report details the magnitude of the growth and the changes in demographic composition, focusing on 2015 and 2040.

This report is also a part of a larger project that builds on the pioneering work that was jointly published in 1993, *The State of Asian Pacific America, Policy Issues to the Year 2020*, by LEAP (Leadership Education for Asian Pacifics) and the UCLA Asian American Studies Center. As with that edited volume, we believe that it is critical to understand key characteristics of the future population of Asian Americans, particularly by nativity and age. Doing so enables us to better understand Asian American concerns and priorities, gain potential insights into the nature of social relations among demographic subgroups of Asian Americans, and speculate on their political and economic contributions to the nation.

While others have made projections of the Asian American population, this project provides details not available elsewhere (Pew Research Center, 2012). Rather than using a simple linear extrapolation for all Asian Americans and Pacific Islanders, collapsing Asian Americans with "others," or reporting only for "Asians Alone," this project utilizes demographic projection techniques that enhance the most recent 2014 National Population Projections by the U.S. Census Bureau.[3] The project also takes into account differences in racial classifications over time[4] and utilizes statistical models to project the absolute and relative size of the Asians who are American citizens through birth (U.S.-born or native-born).[5]

The resource paper is organized into five sections. The first section examines the historical rapid growth of the Asian American population in the latter half of the twentieth century, which has been shaped by the elimination of racially biased immigration restrictions. The second section presents the projected continuing growth, which will increase to approximately 10 percent of the total U.S. population in the mid-2040s. The third section examines the secular shift by nativity (U.S.-born vs. foreign-born). With renewed large-scale immigration, this U.S.-born segment went from being a large majority to a small minority of the Asian American population in the final three decades of the last century. However, this decline in relative share is projected to change in the next quarter of a century, with U.S.-born reaching parity with the foreign-born by the 2040s. Section four examines the distribution by age. Section five examines the growth of multiracial Asians. Interracial marriages have increased over the last quarter century, and that trend will continue into the future. One of the consequences is a higher growth rate in the number of those who are part Asian American, who will make up about a quarter of the net population increase between 2010 and 2040.

Historical Background

Immigration laws have been the single most important factor determining the size of the Asian American population.[6] For more than a century following the latter part of the nineteenth century, Asian immigration was severely restricted due to anti-Asian policy. The Naturalization Act of 1870 excluded Asians from receiving citizenship, and the Chinese Exclusion Act of 1882 and subsequent renewals barred the entry of Chinese laborers. The next major wave of Asian immigration from Japan led to the Gentlemen's Agreement of 1907, under which the Japanese government limited the emigration of its people to the United States. The Asiatic Barred Zone Act of 1917 prohibited all immigrations from additional regions in Asia, and the Immigration Act of 1924 included sections that completely exclude immigration from Asia. Racially motivated legislation, in effect, stemmed meaningful Asian immigration, keeping the Asian American population in the United States artificially low.

Ironically, the tide of restrictive immigration turned at the very same time that anti-Asian prejudices peaked. In 1942, President Franklin D. Roosevelt created the War Relocation Authority, which led to the mass incarceration of Japanese Americans (see U.S. Immigration Center, n.d.). Starting during World War II, the United States began relaxing restrictions, in part to its response to an alliance with China. In 1943, the Chinese Exclusion Act was repealed, a largely symbolic gesture because Chinese immigration was limited to 105 visas a year. The postwar period saw the enactment of the War Brides Act, which allowed many Chinese to bypass the visa quota, entering as spouses, natural children, and adopted children of U.S. military personnel. The 1952 Immigration and Nationality Act ended the Asian immigration exclusion and allowed Asians to naturalize. At the same time, the quotas for Asians remained disproportionately small.

Asians finally got on equal footing in the mid-1960s, with the Immigration and Naturalization Act, which was a product of both the domestic struggle for racial justice[7] and the global struggle for cold war legitimacy with newly independent postcolonial third-world nations.[8] In 1965, the United States adopted the Immigration and Naturalization Act, which abolished the discriminatory national origins quota system, and replaced it with a preference system that was based on skills and family ties to U.S. citizens and permanent residents. It established an annual cap of 270,000 immigrants per year with no more than twenty thousand from any single country. In 1975, the United States adopted the Indochinese Migration and Refugee Assistance Act, allowing some two hundred thousand Cambodians and Vietnamese to enter the United States under a special parole status. The Immigration Reform and Control Act of 1986 allowed undocumented persons who resided in the United States continuously since January 1, 1982, to apply for legal status. The Immigration Act of 1990 increased the annual visa cap to seven hundred thousand, nearly tripling it, for the next three years, and 675,000 for every year after (ibid.).

The elimination of racially biased restrictions, along with later political refugee policies for those displaced by the ending of the war in Southeast Asia, led to a renewal of significant immigration from Asia, which can be seen in Figure 1. Each decade has seen an increase in legal immigration (those who receive permanent resident status). Over the last few years, Asian immigration has surpassed that of Latino immigration (Pew Research Center, 2012). The U.S. Census Bureau projects a continuation of high levels of net migration for Asians (2015a).[9]

Figure 1. Legal Immigration from Asia (in thousands)

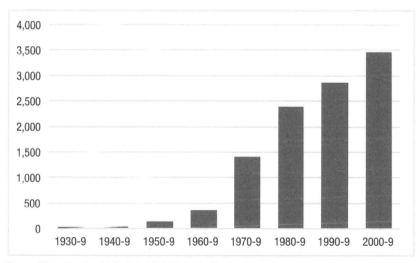

Source: Office of Immigration Statistics' 2013 Yearbook of Immigration Statistics

Asian American Population Projections

The macrolevel demographic impacts of a half century of immigration under the 1965 act and its projected continuation can be seen in Figure 2. The historical trend line is based on the old census racial categories, which allowed an individual to report only one race, and the projected line is based on the new census categories, which allow individuals to report one or more races. The latter is able to capture those of multiracial background.[10] The impact of the legal change is evident in the approximately tenfold increase in the Asian American population between 1970 and 2010, growing at nearly twenty times faster than the total U.S. population. The majority of the growth came both from the wave of immigrants and their U.S.-born children.

Figure 2. Growth of Asian Americans (in thousands)

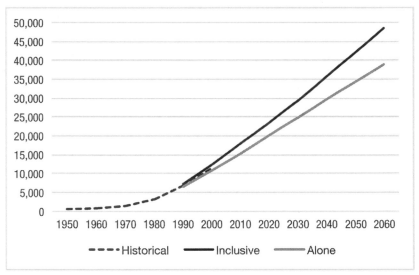

Source: Based on U.S. Census Bureau's 2014 National Population Projections and authors' projections

The Asian American population is projected to continue to grow rapidly, roughly doubling its numbers from 2010 to the early 2040s. The Asian American inclusive count includes both Asians alone and Asians in combination with another race. The Asian American population has been the fastest-growing racial group in America in recent years, and is projected to be the fastest-growing racial group over the next quarter century (see Figure 3; Pew Research Center, 2012). While the total U.S. population will increase by 18 percent, it will be superseded in growth rate by blacks at 33 percent, Hispanics at 61 percent, and Asian Americans at 74 percent.

Figure 3. 2015–40 Increase

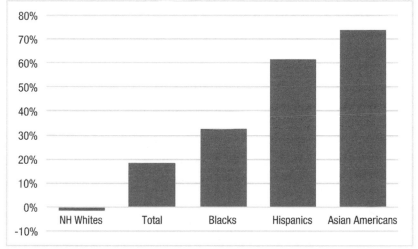

Source: Based on U.S. Census Bureau's 2014 National Population Projections and authors' projections

The differential growth rate by race will make Asian Americans an increasing share of the total U.S. population. As shown in Figure 4, their share increased from about 0.5 percent in 1960 to 5 percent by 2010. By the mid-2040s, Asian Americans will comprise about a tenth of the total U.S. population.

Figure 4. Asian Americans as a Percent of Total

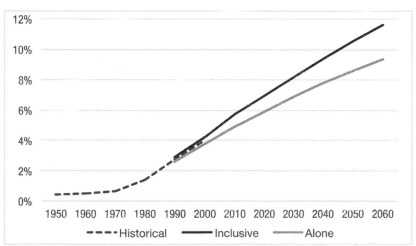

Source: Based on U.S. Census Bureau's 2014 National Population Projections and authors' projections

Distribution by Age

Figure 5 depicts the distribution of the Asian American population in 2015 and 2040. There is a distinctive bulge among prime working age adults, noticeably among younger adults (25–34 years old) in 2015 and extending up to age forty-four in 2040.

Figure 5. Asian American Age Distribution

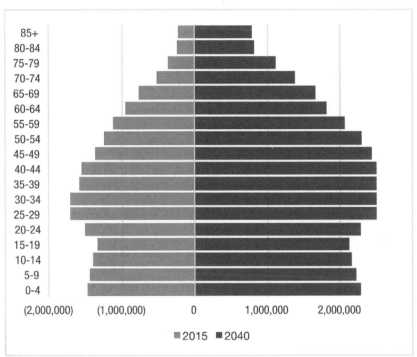

Source: Based on U.S. Census Bureau's 2014 National Population Projections and authors' projections

Like the nation as a whole, the Asian American population will age over time (Ortman, Velkoff, and Hogan, 2014), which will shape policy and other priorities. The median age of the Asian American population will increase from thirty-three years old in 2015 to thirty-seven years old in 2040. While all age groups will increase in absolute numbers, there are noticeable differences in the relative share. Youth (persons seventeen and younger) will decline from 25 percent to 22 percent, while elderly (persons sixty-five and older) will increase from 10 percent to 16 percent. Unlike the total population, there will be no aging "baby boom bulge" in 2040 among Asian Americans, due to their immigration history.

Figure 6. Share of 2015–40 Growth by Age

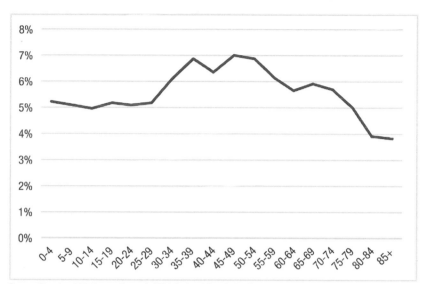

Source: Based on U.S. Census Bureau's 2014 National Population Projections and authors' projections

Figure 6 provides the share of 2015–40 net absolute growth by age groups. This graph shows that working age adults will have larger than average share of net increase, while the elderly will have a lower share of the net increase.[11] However, because there are differences in the base population for each age group, the growth rates are different for each age group. While the growth over the next quarter century is 74 percent, the elderly segment will experience an extraordinarily higher rate (178 percent). This is due to two factors: the small absolute base of elderly in 2015 and the aging of Asian Americans.

Asian Americans by Nativity

Immigration has had a dramatic effect on the absolute and relative size of the Asian American population, and has transformed the group's demographic composition (see Figure 7). Before the 1965, approximately two-thirds of Asian Americans were U.S.-born. After 1965 Immigration Act, the proportion flipped. By the end of the twentieth century, immigrants made up about two-thirds (69 percent of Asian Alone and 63 percent of Asian Inclusive).[12]

Since the start of the twenty-first century, there has been a reversal in the trend in the composition by nativity. The proportion that is U.S.-born is now increasing due to the fact that natural increase[13] has started to outweigh net migration minus immigrant deaths.[14] This new emerging trend is projected to continue over the next quarter century, slowly pushing up the U.S.-born share of the Asian American population. By the early 2040s, the U.S.-born segment will reach numerical parity (50/50) with the immigrant segment.

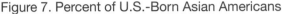

Figure 7. Percent of U.S.-Born Asian Americans

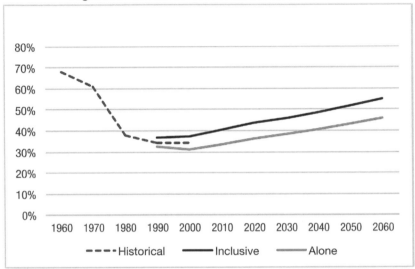

Source: Based on U.S. Census Bureau's 2014 National Population Projections and authors' projections

U.S.-Born Asian Americans

One of the unique characteristics of the U.S.-born segment is the heavy age concentration among the young, which can be seen in Figure 8. In 2015, U.S.-born comprised at least a majority of the age groups up to the twenty to twenty-four year category. A quarter century from now, they will be a majority of groups up to ages twenty-five to twenty-nine, with a larger supermajority among the younger categories; the elderly population will remain predominantly foreign-born, with an increase among the oldest segment.

There is also a recomposition of U.S.-born Asian Americans by generations. A second-generation person has two foreign-born parents, a 2.5-generation person has one foreign-born parent and one U.S.-born parent, and a 3-plus-generation person has two U.S.-born parents.[15] The impact of renewed large-scale immigration after 1965 led to an increase in the relative number of second-generation persons. By 2015, they comprised a large majority (57%) of U.S.-born children and young adults (0-

24 years old). In subsequent years, the pattern will change because of a rapid growth of U.S.-born persons of child-bearing age. By 2040, a majority of U.S.-born children and young adults will be 2.5 and 3-plus generation Asian Americans.

Figure 8. Percent of U.S.-Born among Asian Americans

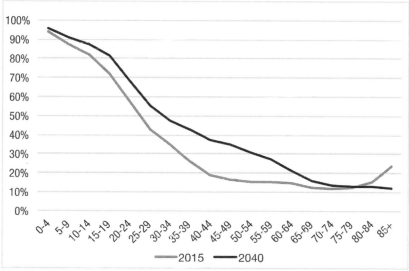

Source: Based on U.S. Census Bureau's 2014 National Population Projections and authors' projections

Multiracial Asian Americans

The growth of the number of multiracial Asian Americans is rooted in an increase in interracial marriages. It has been sixty-six years since the October 1, 1948 California Supreme Court (*Perez v. Lippold*) ruling that antimiscegnation laws violated the Fourteenth Amendment, and forty-eight years since the U.S. Supreme Court's unanimous June 12, 1967 (*Loving v. Virginia*) decision that legalized interracial marriage throughout the United States.

By 2000, 8 percent of marriages were comprised of couples of different races, and the rate increased to 10 percent by 2010. The most common type of interracial marriage was among multiracial/one-race couples (16 percent) and the next most common was non-Hispanic Asian/ non-Hispanic white (14 percent). It is of interest to note that there is a gender differential. For example, in 2010, 22 percent of Asian American women intermarried, while only 9 percent of Asian American men intermarried (Kreider, 2012).

Our analysis of 2013 Public Use Microdata Sample (PUMS) data showed a similar pattern, with an Asian out-marriage rate between 16 and 17 percent, and 23 percent of Asian American women and 9 percent of Asian American men intermarrying. Of those who were recently married between 2009 and 2013, one-third (33 percent) of Asian American women and one-sixth (15 percent) of Asian American men intermarried.[16] The out-marriage rate was more than twice as high for Asian American females than Asian American males.

The number of multiracial children has also grown with the increase in interracial couples. According to the 2000 Census, 6.8 million, or 2.4 percent of the U.S. population, marked that they were of "two or more" races. Of this group, one in four (24 percent) self-identified as part Asian (CensusScope, 2000).

As America becomes more racially diverse, and social taboos against interracial marriage and same-sex marriage fade, multiracial Americans have become the most rapidly growing population in America. Among Asian Americans, multiracial Americans are also the most rapidly growing subpopulation.

Figure 9. Percent of Multiracial Asian Americans

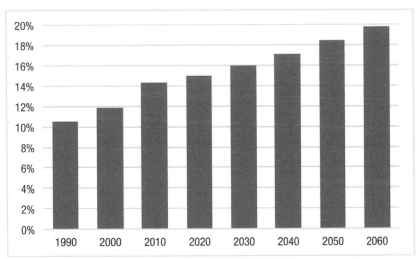

Source: Based on U.S. Census Bureau's 2014 National Population Projections and authors' projections

In 1990, one in ten Asian Americans were multiracial, but by 2060, nearly one in five will be multiracial. The trends and projections of multiracial Asians are displayed in Figure 9. Between 2015 and 2040, the

Asian American Alone population will increase 69 percent, but the multiracial Asian American population will increase by 104 percent, one and half times faster than Asian Americans Alone. In terms of share of net growth between 2015 and 2040, one in five of the net increase among Asian Americans will be from multiracial Asian Americans.

The rapid growth of multiracial Asian Americans will occur among children and young adults. By 2040, preschool children will predominantly be multiracial Asian Americans, and three in ten K–12 youth will be multiracial Asian Americans. Also, by 2040, nearly nine in ten multiracial Asian Americans will be U.S.-born.

Concluding Remarks

America is undergoing a dramatic demographic transformation. By 2043, America will become "majority minority" and reach a new historic social, economic, and political configuration. America will change because Asian Americas are and will be the fastest-growing racial population in America, and Asian America will comprise one of the most diverse segments of what will become America's "multicultural majority."

Asian Americans, who are socially and economically diverse, will contribute to economic growth, both as consumers and as workers. The Selig Center estimates that Asian American buying power equaled $770 billion in 2014, up 180 percent from its 2000 value of $275 billion (Weeks, 2015). Assuming that per capita income remains constant, we estimate that Asian American buying power will be more than $1.25 trillion by 2040. Indeed, if Asian American populations comprised a separate nation, it would rank among the top twenty economies in the world. However, it is not only the size of the Asian American economy that will have an impact. Their contributions to production and consumption will be shaped by its increasingly multigenerational and multiracial composition. Despite this economic trajectory, there is a prospect that will be a significant number of Asian Americans trapped in poverty.

Asian Americans' political importance will grow. In our earlier report, "Asian American Voters to Double by 2040," we found that the electorate will grow from 5.9 million in 2015 to 12.2 million by 2040. Nearly 38 percent of Asian American voters are U.S.-born, but by 2040, nearly half (47 percent) will be (Ong and Ong, 2015). At 7 percent of the registered vote in 2040, political campaigns will want to court the Asian American vote. This will require addressing a diversity of concerns and interests. Many foreign-born Asian American voters could carryover some of the cultural values and concerns of their native countries, and have greater need for "in-language" registration forms, town halls, election booklets, and ballots. In contrast, second- and third-generation Asian Americans are more attuned to mainstream American media, culture, and values, thus their political opinions and attitudes could be shaped by these factors.

The cultural impact will also be profound, although more difficult to chart precisely. Nonetheless, one can extend nascent developments. Asian Americans will continue to serve as a conduit for the advancement of Asian American visual and performing arts in the United States. The absolute and relative growth of second- and subsequent-generation Asian Americans will shift tastes and interests, including ones at the intersection of diverse cultures. The emergence of new individual and collective identities from the increasing number of multiracial Asian Americans will influence the ways Asian Americans are depicted in mass media.

In light of the emerging opportunities and challenges driven by the demographic trajectory, it is critical that we proactively plan for the future.

Acknowledgements

We are indebted to David Armstrong and Jennifer Ortman of the U.S. Census Bureau for their technical review and expertise; and to Chhandara Pech and Silvia Jimenez at UCLA's Center for Neighborhood Knowledge for their technical assistance.

Notes

1. Although the projections treat Asian Americans as a single racial group, it is important to note that it is a very diverse population in terms of ethnicity. E.g., the U.S. Census Bureau reported information for more than two dozen Asian American ethnic groups from the 2010 enumeration.

2. Where both parents are of the same race.

3. The bureau reports projections by nativity only for Asian Americans alone. We supplement those projections with our own estimates for multiracial Asian Americans to produce counts for an inclusive count of both Asian Americans alone and Asian Americans in combination with another race.

4. The project also accounts for the differences in the racial/ethnic categories used for the bureau's population projection models and the categories used for other bureau data sources, such as the decennial census and the American Community Survey. The projections' categories are consistent with those used by the U.S. National Center for Health Statistics. For a discussion on the differences, see National Center for Health Statistics (2015).

5. This also includes a small number who were born in the U.S. territories

or abroad to American citizens. We use microlevel data from the 2010 and 2012 November voter supplement file of the Current Population Survey to estimate the distribution of U.S.-born by generation. For description of that data see U.S. Census Bureau (2015b).

6. There have been three great waves of immigration to the United States, a Northern Europe Wave (1840–89), a Southern/Eastern Europe Wave (1890–1919), and a Modern Era Wave (1965 to present). Immigrants from Latin America comprised 1 percent of the first great wave, 3 percent of the second great wave, and 50 percent of the current great wave. In contrast, immigrants from Asia comprised 2 percent of the first great wave, 2 percent of the second great wave, and 27 percent of the current great wave. For discussion on Asian immigration during the latter period, see Ong, Bonacich, and Cheng (1994).

7. Not coincidentally, that was also the year that saw the enactment of the 1965 Voting Rights Act.

8. The United States was accused of being hypercritical in its effort to promote American-style democracy in developing countries because the United States was not able to ensure equal treatment of its own minority groups. This added pressure, along with that from the civil rights movement, to "put its own house in order."

9. The assumption is that the net Asian migration rate (in migration minus out migration) will increase from 367,000 in 2020 to 400,000 in 2040.

10. We develop a 1990 bridge between the old and new racial classification by estimating an inclusive and alone count based on the 5 percent PUMS. The Asian Alone category includes Asians with only Asian ancestry. The multiracial Asian category includes those who are Asian by race with non-Asian ancestry and those who are not Asian by race with Asian ancestry. We estimate the number of Asians in 2000 as the average of the number of Asian Alone and Asian in Combination with some other race. This estimate is roughly consistent with the ratios of the 1990 estimates and with estimates reported in Ingram et al. (2003).

11. If each of the age categories had the same share, then each would have about 5.6 percent of the net increase.

12. While many of the native-born were second generation, with immigrant parents, there was an emergence of a third generation, with U.S.-born parents. While the number of native-born Asian Americans continue to grow in subsequent decades, the number of new immigrants grew even faster.

13. Natural increase is births minus deaths. U.S.-born have a disproportionately smaller share of natural increase.

14. See "Asian American Voters to Double by 2040" for a method in estimating the nativity of multiracial Asian Americans.

15. The recent distribution by generation is estimated from 2010 and 2012 Current Population Survey. The distribution for 2040 is projected by aging

the 2015 population and projecting the size of the zero to twenty-four-year-old segment by generation. The latter is done by applying a crude fertility rate to child-bearing age adults, with a modest decrease in the rate for U.S.-born individuals.

16. This is similar to the newlywed rate of 31 percent among Asian Americans reported by Passel, Wang, and Taylor (2010).

References

CensusScope. 2000. "2000 Census Multiracial Profile." http://www.censusscope.org/us/chart_multi.html (accessed February 17, 2016).

Ingram, D. D., Parker, J. D., Schenker, N., Weed, J. A., Hamilton, B., Arias, E., and J. H. Madans. 2003. "United States Census 2000 Population with Bridged Race Categories." National Center for Health Statistics. *Vital Health Stat*, Series 2, Number 135, 56 pages.

Kreider, Rose M. 2012. "A Look at Interracial and Interethnic Married Couple Households in the U.S. in 2010." *Random Samplings*, the official blog of the U.S. Census, 28 April.

LEAP. 1993. *The State of Asian Pacific America: Policy Issues to the Year 2020*. Los Angeles: LEAP Asian Pacific American Public Policy Institute and UCLA Asian American Studies Center.

National Center for Health Statistics. 2015. "U.S. Census Populations with Bridged Race Categories." Center for Disease Control and Prevention. http://www.cdc.gov/nchs/nvss/bridged_race.htm (accessed February 17, 2016).

Ong, Paul, Bonacich, Edna, and Lucie Cheng, eds. 1994. *The New Asian Immigration in Los Angeles and Global Restructuring*. Philadelphia: Temple University Press.

Ong, Paul and Elena Ong. 2015. "The Future of Asian America in 2040: Asian American Electorate to Double." UCLA Center for the Study of Inequality and Asian Pacific American Institute for Congressional Studies. http://luskin.ucla.edu/sites/default/files/AA2040_report.pdf (accessed February 17, 2016).

Ortman, Jennifer M., Velkoff, Victoria A., and Howard Hogan. 2014. "An Aging Nation: The Older Population in the United States." Population Estimates and Projections, Current Population Reports, U.S. Census Bureau.

Passel, Jeffrey S., Wang, Wendy, and Paul Taylor. 2010. *Marrying Out: One-in-Seven New U.S. Marriages Is Interracial or Interethnic Marrying Out*. Washington, DC: Pew Research Center's Social and Demographic Trends Project.

Pew Research Center. 2012. "The Rise of Asian Americans." April 3, 2013 update. Pew Research Center Social and Demographic Trends, 19 June. http://www.pewsocialtrends.org/2012/06/19/the-rise-of-asian-americans/ (accessed April 12, 2015).

U.S. Census Bureau. 2015a. 2014 National Population Projections. https://www.census.gov/population/projections/data/national/2014.html (accessed April 12, 2015).

———. 2015b. 2014 National Populations Projection Methodology. https://www.census.gov/population/projections/files/methodology/methodstatements14.pdf (accessed April 12, 2015).

U.S. Department of Homeland Security. Office of Immigration Statistics. 2014. "2013 Yearbook of Immigration Statistics." Washington, DC: U.S. Department of Homeland Security. https://www.dhs.gov/sites/default/files/publications/ois_yb_2013_0.pdf (accessed April 12, 2016).

U.S. Immigration Center. n.d.. Asian American History Timeline. http://www.us-immigration.com/asian-american-history-timeline/ (accessed April 12, 2015).

Weeks, Matt. 2015. "Asians, Hispanics driving U.S. economy forward, according to UGA study." http://news.uga.edu/releases/article/2015-multicultural-economy-report/ (accessed March 29, 2016).

JONATHAN ONG is a data analyst and statistical programmer. He has worked and published on the socioeconomic status of American Indians in Los Angeles, New York's Chinatown, and fair housing in California. Jonathan is a graduate of UCLA, with a Japanese major and a film minor, and is currently studying computer programming.

PAUL ONG is a professor at UCLA's Luskin School of Public Affairs and UCLA's Asian American Studies Department. He is currently the Director of the UCLA Center for Neighborhood Knowledge, founding editor of *AAPI Nexus: Policy, Practice and Community*, and founding director of the UC AAPI Policy Multi-Campus Research Program. He has conducted research on immigration, civic and political participation, economic status of minorities, welfare-to-work, health workers, urban spatial inequality, and environmental inequality.

ELENA ONG is the Vice President of Ong and Associates, where she is a public policy and public affairs consultant to elected officials and nonprofits. Committed to advancing America's health and economic well-being, she served as the President/CEO of the Asian and Pacific Islander Caucus for Public Health prior to being elected to APHA's Executive Board. Committed to public service, Elena has served in a leadership capacity on several U.S. presidential and gubernatorial campaigns, as the governor's appointed First Vice Chair to the California Commission for Women, as Rob Reiner's appointee to the California Children and Families Commission's TA Advisory Board, and as President of the Los Angeles Women's Appointment Collaboration. A recent CORO Executive Fellow, Elena studied Asian American studies at UC Berkeley prior to earning her BSN/PHN from UC San Francisco, and her masters in health policy and management from the Harvard School of Public Health while cross-enrolled at the Kennedy School of Government.

aapi nexus Vol. 14, No. 1 (Spring 2016): 30-48

Practitioner Essay

Asian American Pacific Islander Economic Justice

Paul M. Ong

Abstract

This essay examines economic inequality and poverty among Asian Americans and Pacific Islanders (AAPIs) and their participation in safety-net programs. Income and wealth disparities have increased dramatically over the last few decades, reaching levels not seen since the 1920s. One of the consequences has been an inability to ameliorate poverty, particularly among children. While Asian Americans have been depicted as outperforming all other racial groups, they have not surpassed non-Hispanic whites after accounting for regional differences in the cost of living. Moreover, a relatively large proportion of AAPIs is at the bottom end of the economic ladder. Many impoverished AAPIs rely on antipoverty programs to survive, but most still struggle because of a frayed safety net. Many experts believe that inequality will persist or worsen; consequently, it is likely that the absolute number of poor AAPIs will grow over the next quarter century. Addressing the problems of societal inequality and AAPI poverty will require political action to rectify underlying structural and institutional flaws, and a renewed commitment to ensuring all have a decent standard of living.

Introduction

This essay examines issues of economic inequality and poverty among AAPIs, with an eye to economic justice policies, particularly those related to the safety net. The essay starts with a discussion of national trends related to the growing gulf between the rich and poor, and implicitly the stagnant and shrinking middle class. An inherent part of economic disparity is the existence of an impoverished segment, and the United States has had mixed results in ameliorating poverty. The next section examines the most recent version of the "model minority," which takes the form of Asian Americans out-performing non-Hispanic whites (NH whites). This overly simplistic notion is wrong conceptually and empirically, and it obscures an important reality of the relatively large proportion of AAPIs at the bottom end of the economic spectrum. The subsequent sections provide insights into the nature of AAPI economic inequality and poverty, in particular the relationship between poor AAPIs and the safety net and the set of public and nonprofit programs designed to help the disadvantaged. Many poor AAPIs still rely on these programs, despite the fact that the safety net is becoming more and more frayed. The essay concludes with some thoughts on the future of inequality and poverty, and the work that is needed to rebuild the safety net and address inequality.

Inequality and Poverty

The last half century has witnessed a widening of the gap between the "haves" and the "have-nots" in the United States and globally. Despite overall economic growth, we are reaching levels of inequality not seen since 1928 (Saez, 2013; Stone et al., 2015). Figure 1 shows the growing economic disparity.

Figure 1. Income Inequality (Household Income Gap)

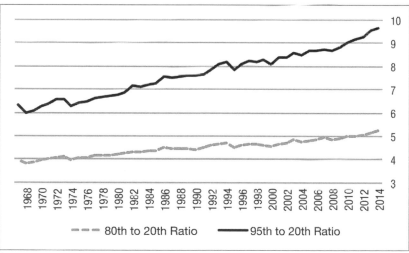

Source: DeNavas-Walt and Proctor, 2015

While there were minor year-to-year fluctuations, the overall secular trend has been upward. The 80th-20th ratio captures the income gap between the top fifth and bottom fifth of all households.[1] A larger ratio indicates a greater disparity. Between 1968 and 2014, that index increased from 3.2 to 5.2. Even more troubling is the increase in income spread between the top 5 percent and the bottom fifth (95th-20th ratio), which climbed from 6.0 to 9.6. Much of the inequality we see is a result of disparities in earnings. An extreme but illustrative example of inequality can be seen in the CEO-to-worker pay ratio, which increased from 58 in 1989 to 352 in 2007 (Mishel and Sabadish, 2012).

An equally important element of economic inequality is wealth disparity, which is substantially more maldistributed than income. Financial and tangible assets have always been highly concentrated, and have become more so in recent decades. For example, the share of wealth held by the top 10 percent increased from 63 percent in 1963 to 73 percent in 2009, while the share held by the bottom half of the population fell from a low of 4 percent to only 2 percent, respectively (Kennickell, 2011). Recent data also show that the richest 5 percent of households control the majority of stocks (Wolff, 2012). Moreover, there is a pronounced racial dimension to the wealth gap, with minorities having markedly fewer assets than whites (Shapiro, Meschede, and Osoro, 2013).

Poverty represents the bottom end of inequality and has been of primary policy concern because being impoverished is defined as not having sufficient income to support a socially acceptable standard of living. Being in poverty status is defined as those falling below the federal poverty line (FPL), which is $11,770 for an individual and $24,250 for a family of four in 2016. The nation's ability to lift people out of poverty has been rather mixed. From 1959 to 1973, the poverty rate decreased by more than half, falling from 22.4 percent to 11.1 percent, due to a combination of trickle-down economics and antipoverty programs. Subsequent years, unfortunately, have witnessed a reversal, with the rate climbing to a high of 15.2 percent. Since then, the rate has fluctuated with the business cycle, and has hovered around 14 percent to 15 percent. The elderly have fared much better, with their poverty rate declining by more than two-thirds, from more than 35 percent in 1959 to less than 10 percent in recent years. Children have not fared as well. While their rates initially fell from 27.3 percent in 1959 to a nadir of 14 percent in 1969, the rate has increased, with about one-in-five living in poverty over the last decade (20 percent).

Poverty also has a spatial dimension. The poor have become increasingly segregated. Since 2000, the number of persons residing in poor neighborhoods (where more than 20 percent of the residents are below the FPL) increased by a third (Kneebone, Nadeau, and Berube, 2011), and there has been a corresponding increase for those living in extremely impoverished neighborhoods (where more than 40 percent of the residents are below the FPL) (Aliprantis and Oliver, 2011; Bishaw, 2011). Research has shown that this spatial divide tends to persist over time and across generations (Sampson and Sharkey, 2008; Wilson, 1987).

AAPIs' Problematic Economic Position

How AAPIs, particularly Asian Americans, fit into the structure of economic inequality has been contentious and overly simplified. Much of the debate has focused on racial disparities, with analysts and the media depicting Asian Americans as being the most successful, even more so than NH whites. Some have interpreted this purported accomplishment as evidence that the United States remains a land of opportunity, so long as one puts in the required personal effort and adheres to the correct cultural values, enabling this minority group to overcome racial discrimination.

The depiction of Asian Americans being at the top of the racial economic ladder has been widely portrayed by the media. For example, *The Atlantic* reported when breaking down census data by race, "Asian Americans continue to lead in household income" (Lam, 2014). The same images are used to depict racial differences in wealth. One Bloomberg article clustered Asian Americans with whites, opposite blacks and Hispanics, emphasizing that Asian Americans have performed better than all other groups (Sunstein, 2015). According to CNBC, this trajectory would eventually "eclipse whites as the wealthiest group of Americans" (Lee, 2015). Of course, these media reports are not simply an imagined stereotype, but are based on research conducted by reputable organizations such as the St. Louis Federal Reserve Bank (Boshara, Emmons, and Noeth, 2015) and Pew Research Center (Kochhar, Taylor, and Fry, 2011; Pew Research Center, 2013a; Pew Research Center, 2013b). In addition, these and other researchers have relied on data from the U.S. Census Bureau and other governmental agencies. This "model minority" stereotype is not new (Petersen, 1966, 180), and "model minority 2.0" has further elevated Asian Americans to a lofty pinnacle that has negative rhetorical implications for other minorities and socioeconomic policy.

The problem is not that the statistics are manufactured, but that reporters and researchers fail to adequately disaggregate the data (Ong, 1993, 1994; Watanabe, 2015). On a conceptual and theoretical level, the stereotype fails to recognize a crucial and pivotal factor. Asian American success is fundamentally rooted in the legal construction of the population, where immigration regulation and practices favored the highly educated (Hing, 1993; Lee and Zhou, 2015; Ong, Bonacich, and Cheng, 1994). This creaming of the top echelon and educational elites of Asia translates into the development of an economically successful Asian American population. Moreover, the stereotype fails to acknowledge that many Asian Americans continue to face both wage discrimination (race and gender) and a glass ceiling.

A more careful analysis of the data reveals a much more nuanced picture. Geographic distribution is an important factor because AAPIs are highly concentrated in major urban areas. Nine consolidated metropolitan areas (Boston, Chicago, Honolulu, Houston, Los Angeles, New York, San Francisco Bay Area, Seattle, and Washington, D.C.) house more than three-fifths (60 percent) of AAPIs (alone) but only a little more than a quarter of non-AAPIs (26 percent). One important economic reality is that firms in these large metropolitan areas must offer higher compensating wages to offset higher cost of living, particularly higher housing cost (Renwick, 2011). Consequently, it takes more income in these locations to maintain the same standard of living. Average household income in these metropolitan areas is more than a quarter higher than for the nation (27 percent), but the cost of living is even higher. The net result is that comparing AAPI and NH whites at the national level is inherently biased. While median Asian American household income is about 25 percent more than median NH white household income using national statistics, it is on the average only 3.5 percent higher in the nine metropolitan areas. In Los Angeles and New York, which have the two largest Asian American populations, it is 3.7 percent and 4.5 percent lower. Pacific Islanders are even lower. Using national statistics, median Pacific Islander household income is 10 percent lower than that for NH whites. In the nine consolidated areas, it is 22.8 percent lower. The geographically adjusted statistics hardly show that AAPIs are "out whiting whites."

Another major blind spot in the "out whiting whites" narrative is the enormous economic heterogeneity within the AAPI population, which in turn make AAPIs disproportionately overrepresented at the bottom relative to NH whites. This can be seen in Figure 2, which reports the parity index by household income categories nationally and for the major metropolitan areas. The index is calculated as the percent of AAPI households in that category divided by the percent of NH whites in that category. For example, 7.2 percent of all AAPI households in the nation and 5.9 percent of all NH white households in the nation had less than $10,000 in annual income, and the corresponding parity index (AAPIs relative to NH whites) is 1.23. In other words, AAPIs are overrepresented at the bottom end. National data also show that AAPIs are overrepresented at the high end. This duality can be interpreted as AAPIs being more bimodal in income distribution relative to NH whites. The numbers for the nine metropolitan areas reveal a different picture. AAPIs are overrepresented in the two bottom income categories and minimally overrepresented in the top categories. In Los Angeles and New York, AAPIs are on the average slightly underrepresented in the top categories.

Figure 2. AAPI-NH White Parity Index by Household Income Categories

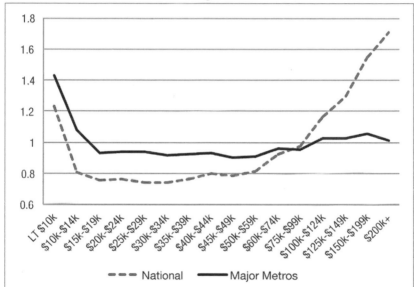

Source: Tabulations by author from 2011–2013 American Community Survey Data

Analyzing temporal change in household income reveals that the inequality among AAPIs has increased, much like that for the nation as a whole. This analysis uses the same income indicators introduced earlier in the essay to discuss inequality in the United States. The AAPI ratio between the 80th and 20th percentiles increased from 5.0 in 1999 to 5.36 in 2014, and the 95th to 20th ratio increased from 8.8 to 10.0.[2] The increase in disparity is due to a decline in the 20th percentile (-2.4 percent in constant dollars) and an increase in the 80th and 95th percentile (4.6 percent and 10 percent, respectively). In other words, the national trend in growing inequality is also taking place among AAPIs.

AAPI Inequality and Poverty

Overrepresentation at the bottom end translates into an AAPI poverty rate that is higher than for NH whites, although lower than for the total population (see Figure 3). The higher rates for all are driven up by the extremely high poverty rates among African Americans and Latinos (26 percent and 23.6 percent, respectively). The net result is that AAPIs occupy a middle ground between the dominant NH white population and other people of color. Combining all AAPIs into a single group, however, obscures significant differences in economic status among ethnic groups.

Figure 3. Poverty Rates

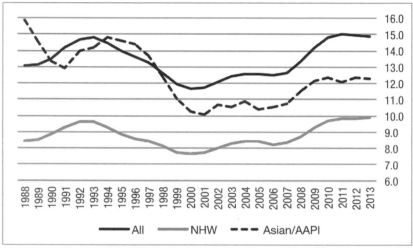

Source: DeNavas-Walt and Proctor, 2015

The AAPI rubric is a panethnic construction that was established in part for the purpose of collecting and reporting statistics for major racial categories, but this approach has severe limitations. As other authors in this volume have argued, it is important to disaggregate the data in order to understand the systematic internal diversity. Median income for Asian Americans range from a high of more than $98,000 (Asian Indians) to a low of about $35,000 (Burmese), a ratio of more than three to one. The ethnic disparity among Asian Americans in terms of poverty is even greater, with the rate for the most impoverished group being approximately six times that of the least impoverished one (41.5 percent for Burmese vs. 7 percent for Filipinos). Overall, median income for Pacific Islanders is considerably lower than that for Asian Americans, a difference of nearly $20,000 or 28 percent of the Asian American median, and the Pacific Islander poverty rate is 1.6 times as high. The ethnic differences among Pacific Islander ethnic groups are not as great as the ethnic differences among Asian American ethnic groups, but are nonetheless substantial, particularly for poverty where the highest Pacific Islander rate (Microneasians) is three times that of the lowest Pacific Islander rate (Fijians and Melanesians).

It is important to note that the economic status of the most disadvantaged Asian American groups is a by-product of our immigration policies. Many Southeast Asians came as political refugees who experienced extensive war traumas and lacked education and transferable skills. While the United States initially promised resources to help them to become economically self-sufficient (The Indochina Migration and Refugee Assistance Act, 1975; U.S. Department of Health and Human Services, 2012), most were abandoned to the welfare system, which failed to provide the appropriate programs to help them transition to meaningful employment (Ong and Ishikawa, 2006; Truong, 2007). The problem is not just the impoverishment of the first-generation refugees. Many refugee populations are experiencing intergenerational immobility, with a disproportionately high proportion of the 1.5 generation (the refugees who came to the United States as refugees) and second generation being trapped in the lower economic strata (Portes and Fernandez-Kelly, 2008; Portes and Zhou, 1993; Zhou and Xiong, 2005).

There are two other salient characteristics of AAPI poverty. First, poverty rates not only vary by ethnicity but also by age (DeNavas-Walt and Proctor, 2015). The 2014 rate for AAPI elderly is nearly twice as high as that for NH whites and one-and-a-half times as high as for the total population (15 percent, 8 percent, and 10 percent, respectively). Poor AAPI elderly tend to be immigrants with minimal retirement benefits. Second, although the rate for AAPI children is roughly comparable to those for NH whites and lower than for the total population (12 percent, 12 percent, and 21 percent, respectively), there are pockets of very high poverty among Southeast Asian and Pacific Islander children, with well more than a quarter living below the FPL. Third, AAPI poverty has a spatial dimension. Nearly half (48 percent) of AAPIs in poverty reside in poor neighborhoods, areas where at least one-fifth of all residents fall below the FPL. One in eight (13 percent) reside in "underclass" neighborhoods, areas where at least two-fifths of all residents fall below the FPL.

AAPIs and the Safety Net

The economic and social safety net is critical to ameliorating some of the hardships faced by the poor. Over the last quarter century, some antipoverty programs faced dramatic fiscal cuts and others have been transformed, due in part to shifting ideology about the role of the state in helping the poor. A primary example is the change in public assistance. For example, the Personal Responsibility and Work Opportunity Reconciliation Act of 1996 transformed the preexisting entitlement program (Aid to Families with Dependent Children, or AFDC) into a transition-to-work program (Temporary Assistance for Needy Families, or TANF). The number of families on AFDC/TANF dropped from 5.05 million in 1994 to 1.75 million in 2013 (Falk, 2016), and benefit amounts have declined by about a fifth to levels below 50 percent of the FPL (Center on Budget and Policy Priorities, 2015). The transition-to-work programs have been problematic for many because TANF failed to provide adequate support to prepare recipients for meaningful employment, while they have limited lifetime income assistance to five years. This is particularly true for female-headed families (ibid.). At the same time, the government expanded the earned income tax credit (EITC), a tax provision targeted to employed low- and moderate-income taxpayers. EITC is designed as an incentive for low-income people to stay off welfare by working, and it has an important countercyclical effect: partially offsetting earnings losses during economic downturns (Jones, 2014). Started in 1975, it is now the nation's largest antipoverty program (Ault and Bucknor, 2014), covering more than 27.5 million tax filers in 2014, up from 19.5 million in 1996 (U.S. Internal Revenue Service, 2015). Twenty-six states and the District of Columbia have established their own EITCs to supplement the federal credit. The average amount, however, is not substantial, and the national average was about $2,400 in 2014, roughly a tenth of the FPL for a family of four.

Despite the decline in and transformation of the safety net, anti-poverty programs are nonetheless important to poor AAPIs. Participation varies across both ethnic groups and programs. While there are no comprehensive statistics, it is possible to derive an overall sense of the phenomenon by mining several data sources. The American Community Survey provides information on cash assistance (welfare, primarily TANF) and food stamps. Eight percent of Asian American households and 22 percent of Pacific Islander households participate in food stamps, with rates varying by ethnicity, from a low of 7 percent to a high of 45 percent. Not surprisingly, food-stamp usage is correlated with the poverty rate, with a few exceptions due to cultural, linguistic, and eligibility barriers. The proportion receiving cash assistance is remarkably low relative to poverty—2 percent of Asian American households and 6 percent of Pacific Islander households—not surprising given the retrenchment associated with TANF. There are tremendous ethnic differences, corresponding to poverty rates, as well as other factors such as refugee status and exclusion due to exhausting lifetime benefits.

The 2015 March Supplement of the Current Population Survey provides information on EITC and the National School Lunch Program (NSLP). According to one estimate for the 2013 tax year, more than one million Asian American workers with 1.5 million children filed for EITC, with refunds averaging about $1,400 (Center on Budget and Policy Priorities, 2015). Overall, 16 percent of Asian American households and 25 percent of Pacific Islander households reported having EITC income, compared with a national average of 16 percent. Not surprisingly, the rates vary systematically by ethnicity. NSLP lunches are provided free or at a reduced price for students from low-income households (for a family of four for the 2014–15 school year, below $23,850 for free meals and below $44,123 for reduced meals, with slightly higher thresholds for Alaska and Hawaii) (U.S. Department of Agriculture, 2014). This program is considered vital to learning because a hungry child is less attentive, with the additional benefit of improving children's overall health. Roughly 8 percent of Asian American households and 18 percent of Pacific Islander households have at least one child participating, compared with a national average of 9 percent. Again, there are significant ethnic variations.

Another essential need is subsidized housing. Among Asian American households in poverty, 74 percent do not own a home, and the corresponding figure for Pacific Islander households is 80 percent. Among poverty renters, 67 percent of Asian Americans and 82 percent of Pacific Islanders pay more than 30 percent of their income for housing, and 54 percent and 61 percent pay more than 50 percent. Although accurate counts of the homelessness are elusive, the U.S. Department of Housing and Urban Development's (HUD's) Point-in-Time unduplicated count of sheltered and unsheltered homeless persons provides some insights. Asian Americans accounted for only 1.1 percent of those enumerated in 2015, far below its (Asian American alone) 5.5 percent of the total population. What is astonishing is that Pacific Islanders accounted for 1.6 percent, eight times the Pacific Islanders share of the total population (0.2 percent for Pacific Islanders alone). Equally disturbing is the fact that homeless Pacific Islanders are more likely to be "unsheltered" than all homeless persons (43 percent and 31 percent, respectively).

HUD provides rental housing assistance for about 4.7 million low-income families, elders, and persons with disabilities through three main programs: Section 8 housing choice voucher (HCV) (2.4 million), project-based rental assistance (1.2 million), and public housing (1.1 million). The HCV program provides subsidies to households renting from participating private landlords. The HCV program is considered a tenant-based program, allowing households the opportunity to select from available market units. For project-based subsidized housing, HUD contracts with nonprofit and for-profit housing developers to supply units to needy households, therefore subsidies are tied to units and housing sites, which limit locational choice. Public housing is rental housing owned and managed by public housing authorities, with units usually located in large multiunit complexes. For all three programs, households generally pay 30 percent of their income on housing, and the difference is subsidized. AAPIs do participate in all three programs. According to statistics from HUD, non-Hispanic AAPIs comprise 3 percent of those in public housing, 3 percent of those receiving HCVs, and 5 percent in project-based housing. Although participation has eased the housing burden on these AAPI households, we do not know if they are proportionately represented among subsidized residents (U.S. Department of Housing and Urban Development, 2016c). Moreover, it is likely that there are many more in need but unable to secure a unit. Housing needs far outstrip the number of subsidized rental units, thus forcing applicants to wait months and even years (Quigley, 2007; U.S. Department of Housing and Urban Development, 1999).

Given the spatial concentration of many poor AAPIs in economically disadvantaged neighborhoods, place-based antipoverty programs can complement the people-based strategies listed earlier. This is a community development strategy that targets resources, financial incentives, and capacity-building efforts to some of the most disadvantaged areas (Ong and Loukiatou-Sideris, 2006). The goal is to improve more immediate economic opportunities for adults and long-term educational achievements for children. At times, this approach incorporated efforts to increase civic and political engagement with the objective of giving residents more control. The place-based approach has been used by government in the form of model cities in the 1960s and early 1970s, and more recently as Empowerment Zones, Enterprise Communities and Promise Neighborhoods (Arnstein, 1969; Moynihan, 1969; U.S. Department of Education, 2016; U.S. Department of Housing and Urban Development, 2016a and 2016b). Private foundations have also supported place-based efforts, starting with the Ford Foundation's pioneering "Gray Area" project in the 1950s and 1960s (O'Connor, 1996), and more recently by The California Endowment's "Building Healthy Communities" initiative, in 14 neighborhoods (The California Endowment, 2016).

AAPIs can benefit from placed-based programs because they are in some of the targeted neighborhoods. For example, the Los Angeles Promise Zone includes Thai Town and the Thai Community Development Center (CDC) is a participating organization (City of Los Angeles, 2014). Over a quarter (26%) of the residents in the Saint Paul Promise Neighborhood are Asian Americans (Regan, 2012). Several of The California Endowment "Building Health Communities" sites contain substantial number of AAPIs. For example, they comprise about a fifth of the population in the San Diego and Long Beach target areas. The latter contains Cambodia Town, home to nearly 18,000 Cambodian (Pastor, Ito, and Perez, 2014). There is, however, a caveat. While AAPIs may be a part of place-based sites, they may not be participating at rates proportionate to their share of the population (Regan, 2012). Meaningful participation requires active cross-racial collaboration, a strategy that is challenging but very much needed.

Future of Economic Justice

Although it is impossible to predict the future course of economic inequality and poverty, many experts and the general public do not foresee a bright future. The high level of inequality will continue and may even increase. This will create a crisis of the middle class due to the inability to maintain their previous standard of living (Erickson, 2014) There is also a belief that future generations will not be better off (Jones, Cox, and Navarro-Rivera, 2014). Growing inequality will trickle down to those at the bottom. According to Neilsen Media Research Firm, the near poor—households with less than 1.5 (times) the poverty line—will grow by more than 10 percent from 2009 to 2020, and by nearly 70 percent by 2050 (Anderson, 2009). According to one of the foremost experts on poverty projects: "the share of poor persons who are elderly will rise . . . many men will confront poverty in the years to come because of poor labor market prospects" and poverty will geographically disperse beyond the inner city (Plotnick, 2016). Even if income and wealth disparities do not increase, they are already at levels not healthy for society.

AAPIs will be trapped in this inequality trajectory. As we have seen, economic disparities and poverty are present within this population. If the current poverty rate continues, then the number of AAPIs (alone) in poverty will grow from an estimated 2.2 million in 2015 to 3.7 million in 2040. Of course, this is extremely speculative, and many factors will alter the trajectory and future composition. There will be some improvements over the next few decades from continued economic assimilation of immigrants and the educational achievements of their children, but they may be swimming upstream against the larger economic current reproducing inequality. AAPI millennials are not immune from the forces that undermine the ability to do better than the previous generation, and older AAPIs face an uncertain prospect when they reach retirement age. While trying to precisely project is impossible, the number of poor AAPI will grow, and regardless of the future number, having so many impoverished is unacceptable for a wealthy nation that pledges "justice for all."

Tackling poverty and other inequality challenges will require developing strategies that address the specific needs of AAPIs, while also embracing a broader social justice agenda. The following recommendations are based on both objective economic realities and normative values.

One, we rebuild the safety net. This is necessary to being a compassionate and fair society. As Mahatma Ghandi stated, "A nation's greatness is measured by how it treats its weakest members." This requires a commitment to redistribution to ensure a socially acceptable minimum standard of living, not because of pity, but because it is a form of social justice that we would want for ourselves in the absence of privilege. It is likely that AAPIs will continue to have unique needs, particularly among the elderly and children of AAPI ethnic groups who experience significantly high poverty rates.

Two, we expand opportunities by enhancing individual capabilities. On the long run, we must provide the skills and knowledge that enable all people to pursue meaningful careers and to provide for their families. This includes providing training for the most disadvantaged AAPI immigrants—particularly among the refugee groups—and ensuring equal access to quality education for all children.

Three, we directly address group-based inequality. Economic disparity is not defined solely as differences among individuals. Instead, it is structured along socially constructed groups, including along racial and ethnic lines (Omi and Winant, 2015). Social hierarchies are reinforced by a systematic and institutionalized web of mutually reinforcing discrimination in economic markets. Dismantling this system requires a recommitment to policies rectifying past wrongs and protecting against biases.

Four, we reinstitute a more progressive tax system. The United States has one of the least progressive income tax rates among Western economies, and today's rates for the most affluent are significantly lower than in the 1970s (Greenstone and Looney, 2012). The purpose is to tax according the ability to pay. Moreover, this approach is based on the belief that the economically successful should have an obligation to give back to the society that enabled them to become affluent.

Finally, we support policies that directly address the fundamental forces that have created the current unacceptable level of economic inequality. Not all forms of income and wealth are unacceptable, but there are market imperfections and regulatory failures that enable a few to unjustly accumulate unearned income and wealth. The magnitude and consequences of these structural problems are very evident in the financial gains made by Wall Street before the Great Recession and the devastation that was inflicted on millions during the foreclosure crisis. We should not allow this to happen ever again.

The preceding changes can only come about through concerted political action to move the policy needle. The nation is at a pivotal juncture where inequality, selective stagnation, and uncertainty about the future have created anxiety and anger among the majority of the populous. There is a real danger that demagogues will exploit this economic angst by targeting domestic and international scapegoats. Such a political movement could very well harm AAPIs. As a minority, we can find strength by aligning with others who adhere to a progressive agenda that honors an inclusive and just society. AAPIs should bring their concerns and priorities to the table, but we must go beyond narrow self-interest. The struggle will be hard, and we need to take advantage of the nation's democratic principles despite its plutocratic practice, particularly after the U.S. Supreme Court's "United Citizens," which has opened the political floodgate for the economically powerful to disproportionately influence elections. We and others must be the countervailing force, and this will materialize when we are strategically decisive.

Acknowledgement

I am thankful to Chhandara Pech from UCLA's Center for Neighborhood Knowledge for his ever-efficient assistance in assembling the statistics, Wunai Zhao for checking references, and Elena Ong for her invaluable feedback. Preparation of the background materials on inequality and poverty was supported in part by a grant from the John Randolph Haynes Foundation. I alone am responsible for the content.

Notes

1. The 80th-20th ratio is calculated by dividing the income for a household at the 80th percentile (the amount that separates the most affluent top fifth or richest 20 percent from all other households) by the income for a household at the 20th percentile (the dollar amount that separates the poorest fifth from all other households). Data for 2014 can be used to illustrate how the ratio is calculated. For that year, the 80th percentile was $112,262, and the 20th percentile was $21,432, resulting in a ratio of 5.2. The 95th-20th ratio is calculated in a similar fashion using the income for a household at the 95th percentile to capture the economic status of the richest 5 percent of all households. In 2014, the amount was $206,568, so the corresponding 95th-20th ratio is 9.6.

2. The ratios are based on analysis of the 2000 Decennial PUMS and 2014 ACS PUMS by author.

References

Aliprantis, Dionissi, and Nelson Oliver. 2011. "Recent Trends in Neighborhood Poverty." Federal Reserve Bank of Cleveland. https://www.clevelandfed.org/en/newsroom-and-events/publications/economic-trends/2011-economic-trends/et-20111129-recent-trends-in-neighborhood-poverty.aspx (accessed March 31, 2016).

Anderson, Doug. 2009. "The United States in 2020 a Very Different Place." The Nielson Company. http://www.nielson.com/us/en/insights/news/2009/the-united-states-in-2020-a-very-different-place.html (accessed March 31, 2016).

Arnstein, Sherry R. 1969. "A Ladder of Citizen Participation." *Journal of the American Institute of Planners* 35(4): 216–24.

Ault, Mindy, and Cherrie Bucknor. 2014. "Poverty and the Earned Income Tax Credit." *The Public Purpose* 12. http://observer.american.edu/spa/publicpurpose/upload/2014-public-purpose-earned-income-tax-credit-ault-bucknor.pdf (accessed March 15, 2016).

Bishaw, A. 2011. *Areas with Concentrated Poverty: 2006–2010.* Washington, DC: U.S. Census Bureau. http://www.census.gov/prod/2011pubs/acsbr10-17.pdf (accessed March 31, 2016).

Boshara, Ray, Emmons, William R., and Bryan J. Noeth. 2015. "The Demographics of Wealth How Age, Education and Race Separate Thrivers from Strugglers in Today's Economy." Federal Reserve Bank of St. Louis, Essay Series, February. https://www.stlouisfed.org/~/media/Files/PDFs/HFS/essays/HFS-Essay-1-2015-Race-Ethnicity-and-Wealth.pdf (accessed March 31, 2016).

California Endowment, The. 2016. "14 Places." http://www.calendow.org/places/ (accessed March 31, 2016).

Center on Budget and Policy Priorities. 2015. "The Earned Income Tax Credit, the Child Tax Credit, and Asian Amercians." Fact Sheet, 21 July.

City of Los Angeles. 2014. "Los Angeles Promise Zone Partner and Supporter

Directory." Los Angeles: Mayor's Office of Economic Development.

DeNavas-Walt, Carmen, and Bernadette D. Proctor. 2015. "Income and Poverty in the United States: 2014." United States Census Bureau, Current Populatons Report, September. https://www.census.gov/content/dam/Census/library/publications/2015/demo/p60-252.pdf (accessd March 31, 2016).

Erickson, Jennifer. 2014. "The Middle-Class Squeeze: A Picture of Stagnant Incomes, Rising Costs, and What We Can Do to Strengthen America's Middle Class." Center for American Progress. https://www.americanprogress.org/issues/economy/report/2014/09/24/96903/the-middle-class-squeeze/ (accessed March 31, 2016).

Falk, Gene. 2016. "Temporary Assistance for Needy Families (TANF): Size and Characteristics of the Cash Assistance Caseload." Congressional Research Services, Report, 29 January. https://www.fas.org/sgp/crs/misc/R43187.pdf (accessed March 31, 2016).

Greenstone, Michael, and Adam Looney. 2012. "Just How Progressive Is the U.S. Tax Code?" The Brookings Institute, Paper, 13 April. http://www.brookings.edu/blogs/up-front/posts/2012/04/13-tax-greenstone-looney (accessed March 31, 2016).

Hing, Bill Ong. 1993. *Making and Remaking Asian America*. Stanford, CA: Stanford University Press.

Indochina Migration and Refugee Assistance Act of 1975. Pub. L. No. 94-23. 89 Stat. 87 (1975).

Jones, Maggie R. 2014. "Changes in EITC Eligibility and Participation, 2005–2009." U.S. Census Bureau, Working Paper #2014-04, 11 July. https://www.census.gov/srd/carra/Changes_in_EITC_Eligibility_and_Participation_2005-2009.pdf (accessed March 31, 2016).

Jones, Robert P., Cox, Daniel, and Juhem Navarro-Rivera. 2014. *Economic Insecurity Rising Inequality, and Doubts about the Future*. Washington, DC: Public Religion Research Institute.

Kennickell, Arthur B. 2011. "Tossed and Turned: Wealth Dynamics of U.S. Households 2007–2009." The Federal Reserve Board, Working Paper, 7 November. http://www.federalreserve.gov/pubs/feds/2011/201151/201151pap.pdf (accessed March 31, 2016).

Kneebone, Elizabeth, Nadeau, Carey, and Alan Berube. 2011. "The Re-emergence of Concentrated Poverty: Metropolitan Trends in the 2000s." The Brookings Institute, Paper, 3 November. http://www.brookings.edu/research/papers/2011/11/03-poverty-kneebone-nadeau-berube (accessed March 31, 2016).

Kochhar, Rakesh, Taylor, Paul, and Richard Fry. 2011. "Wealth Gaps Rise to Record Highs between Whites, Blacks and Hispanics." Pew Research Center. http://www.pewsocialtrends.org/2011/07/26/wealth-gaps-rise-to-record-highs-between-whites-blacks-hispanics/ (accessed March 31, 2016).

Lam, Bourree. 2014. "Black, White, Asian, Hispanic: The Disparities in Household Income." *The Atlantic*, 16 September. http://www.theatlantic.com/

business/archive/2014/09/black-white-asian-hispanic-the-disparities-in-household-income/380314/ (accessed March 16, 2016).

Lee, Hailey. 2015. "How Asian-Americans Are Transforming the Face of US Wealth." *CNBC*, 15 March. http://www.cnbc.com/2015/03/15/mericans-are-transforming-the-face-of-us-wealth.html (accessed March 31, 2016).

Lee, Jennifer, and Min Zhou. 2015. *The Asian American Achievement Paradox.* New York: Russell Sage.

Mishel, Lawrence, and Natalie Sabadish. 2012. "CEO Pay and the Top 1%: How Executive Compensation and Financial-Sector Pay Have Fueled Income Inequality." Economic Policy Institute, Report, 2 May. http://www.epi.org/publication/ib331-ceo-pay-top-1-percent/ (accessed March 31, 2016).

Moynihan, Daniel P. 1969. *Maximum Feasible Misunderstanding; Community Action in the War on Poverty.* New York: Free Press.

O'Connor, Alice. 1996. "Community Action, Urban Reform, and the Fight against Poverty: The Ford Foundation's Gray Areas Program." *Journal of Urban History* 22(5): 586–625.

Omi, Michael, and Howard Winant. 2015. *Racial Formation in the United States.* New York: Routledge.

Ong, Paul, ed. 1994. *The State of Asian Pacific America: Economic Diversity, Issues and Policies.* Los Angeles: LEAP Asian Pacific American Public Policy Institute and UCLA Asian American Studies Center.

———. 1993. *Beyond Asian American Poverty: Community Economic Development Policies and Strategies.* 2nd ed. Los Angeles: LEAP Asian Pacific American Public Policy Institute.

Ong, Paul, and Hiroshi Ishikawa. 2006. "A Research Agenda: Impacts of Welfare Reform on Asian Americans and Pacific Islanders (AAPIs)." Ralph and Goldy Lewis Center for Regional Policy Studies, Research Paper, June.

Ong, Paul, and Anastasia Loukiatou-Sideris, eds. 2006. *Jobs and Economic Development in Minority Communities.* Philadelphia: Temple University Press.

Ong, Paul, Bonacich, Edna, and Lucy Cheng, eds. 1994. *The New Asian Immigration in Los Angeles and Global Restructuring.* Philadelphia: Temple University Press.

Pastor, Manuel, Ito, Jennifer, and Anthony Perez. 2014. "There's Something Happening Here . . . A Look at The California Endowment's Building Healthy Communities Initiative." USC Program for Environmental and Regional Equity (PERE), Report, February. http://dornsife.usc.edu/assets/sites/242/docs/TCE-BHC-Narrative-PERE.pdf (accessed March 31, 2016).

Petersen, William. 1966. "Success Story: Japanese American Style." *New York Times,* 9 January.

Pew Research Center. 2013a. "Asian-Americans Lead All Others in Household Income." http://www.pewresearch.org/daily-number/asian-americans-lead-all-others-in-household-income/ (accessed March 31, 2016).

———. 2013b. "The Rise of Asian Americans." http://www.pewsocialtrends.org/2012/06/19/the-rise-of-asian-americans/ (accessed March 31, 2016).

Plotnick, Robert D. 2016. "What Will the New Face of American Poverty Look Like?" Big Think. http://bigthink.com/experts-corner/what-will-the-new-face-of-american-poverty-look-like (accessed March 31, 2016).

Portes, Alejandro, and Patricia Fernandez-Kelly, P. 2008. "No Margin for Error: Educational and Occupation Achievement among Disadvantaged Children of Immigrants." *ANNALs of the Academy of Political and Social Science* 620: 12–36.

Portes, Alejandro, and Min Zhou. 1993. "The New Second Generation: Segmented Assimilation and Its Variants." *Annals of the American Academy of Political and Social Science* 530: 74–96.

Quigley, John M. 2007. "Just Suppose: Housing Subsidies for Low-Income Renters." Harvard University Joint Center for Housing Studies, Working Paper, March. http://www.jchs.harvard.edu/sites/jchs.harvard.edu/files/rr07-9_quigley.pdf (accessed March 31, 2016).

Quintilani, Karen. 2014. "A Qualitative Study of the Long Term Impact of Welfare Reform on Cambodian American Families." *Journal of Southeast Asian American Education and Advancement* 9: 1–27.

Regan, Sheila. 2012. "Are Asian Americans Benefiting from NAZ and Saint Paul Promise Neighborhoods?" *Twin Cities Daily Planet*, 5 August. http://www.tcdailyplanet.net/are-asian-americans-benefitting-naz-and-saint-paul-promise-neighborhoods/ (accessed March 31, 2016).

Renwick, Trudi. 2011. *Geographic Adjustments of Supplemental Poverty Measure Thresholds: Using the American Community Survey Five-Year Data on Housing Costs*. Washington, DC: U.S. Census Bureau.

Saez, Emmanual. 2013. *Tables and Figures—Income Tax Statistics*. http://eml.berkeley.edu/~saez/TabFig2012prel.xls (accessed March 31, 2016).

Sampson, Robert J., and Patrick Sharkey. 2008. "Neighborhood Selection and the Social Reproduction of Concentrated Racial Inequality." *Demography* 45(1): 1–29.

Shapiro, Thomas, Meschede, Tatjana, and Sam Osoro. 2013. "The Roots of the Widening Racial Wealth Gap: Explaining the Black-White Economic Divide." Institute on Assets and Social Policy, Policy Brief, February. http://iasp.brandeis.edu/pdfs/Author/shapiro-thomas-m/racialwealthgapbrief.pdf (accessed March 31, 2016).

Stone, Chad, Trisi, Danilo, Sherman, Arloc, and Brandon DeBot. 2015. "A Guide to Statistics on Historical Trends in Income Inequality." Center on Budget and Policy Priorities, Report. www.cbpp.org/files/11-28-11pov.pdf (accessed March 31, 2016).

Sunstein, Cass R. 2015. "Asians Make It Big in America." BloombergView. http://www.bloombergview.com/articles/2015-03-02/why-asian-americans-will-soon-be-the-wealthiest-americans (accessed March 31, 2016).

Truong, Michael H. 2007. "Welfare Reform and Liberal Governance: Disciplining Cambodian-American Bodies." *International Journal of Social Welfare* 16(3): 258–68.

U.S. Department of Agriculture. 2014. "Income Eligibility Guidelines." *Federal Register* 79(43): 12467–69. http://www.fns.usda.gov/sites/default/files/2014-04788.pdf (accessed March 18, 2016).

U.S. Department of Health and Human Services. Office of Refugee Resettlement. 2012. "The Refugee Act." http://www.acf.hhs.gov/programs/orr/resource/the-refugee-act (accessed December 23, 2015).

U.S. Department of Education. Office of Innovation and Improvement. 2016a. "Programs, Promise Neighborhoods." http://www2.ed.gov/programs/promiseneighborhoods/index.html#description (accessed March 18, 2016).

———. 2016b. "Economic Development." http://portal.hud.gov/hudportal/HUD?src=/program_offices/comm_planning/economicdevelopment (accessed March 22, 2016).

———. 2016c. "Picture of Subsidized Households." https://www.huduser.gov/portal/datasets/picture/yearlydata.html (accessed April 1, 2016).

———. 1999. "Waiting in Vain: An Update on America's Housing Crisis." Washington, DC: Government Printing Office. http://*www.huduser.gov/portal/Publications/pdf/HUD-8681.pdf (accessed March 25, 2016).*

U.S. Internal Revenue Service. 2015. "Earned Income Tax Credit Statistics." https://www.irs.gov/Individuals/Earned-Income-Tax-Credit-Statistics (accessed March 24, 2016).

Watanabe, Paul. 2015. "Asian Americans Rise Up the Response to the Pew Report on The Rise of Asian Americans." *AAPI Nexus Journal* 13(1–2): 321–34.

Wilson, William Julius. 1987. *The Truly Disadvantaged: The Inner City, the Underclass, and Public Policy.* Chicago: University of Chicago Press.

Wolff, Edward N. 2012. "The Asset Price Meltdown and the Wealth of the Middle Class." National Bureau of Economic Research, Working Paper No. w18559, November. http://www.nber.org/papers/w18559.pdf (accessed March 31, 2016).

Zhou, Min, and Yang Sao Xiong. 2005. "The Multifaceted American Experiences of the Children of Asian Immigrants: Lessons for Segmented Assimilation." *Ethnic and Racial Studies* 28(6): 1119–52.

PAUL M. ONG is a professor at UCLA's Luskin School of Public Affairs and UCLA's Asian American Studies Department. He is currently the director of the UCLA Center for Neighborhood Knowledge, founding senior editor of *AAPI Nexus: Policy, Practice and Community*, and founding director of the UC AAPI Policy Multi-Campus Research Program. He has conducted research on immigration, civic and political participation, economic status of minorities, welfare-to-work, health workers, urban spatial inequality, and environmental inequality.

aapi nexus Vol. 14, No. 1 (Spring 2016): 49-65

Practitioners Essay

No Data, No Justice:
Moving beyond the Model Minority Myth in K–12 Education

Rita Pin Ahrens and Souvan Lee

As America becomes more ethnically diverse, we must ensure that all students—regardless of race—can reach their full potential. In education, this begins with data. . . . When all students count, all students can succeed.

Marc Morial, President of the National Urban League[1]

Abstract

Due to the "model minority myth," Asian American and Pacific Islander (AAPI) students are often left out of the national discourse on educational equity. As a result, obtaining more data on AAPI students (i.e., data disaggregation) has become the primary civil rights issue in education for AAPIs. This paper examines challenges facing AAPIs in elementary and secondary public schools, passage of the Every Student Succeeds Act, and progress made to disaggregate data on AAPI students. The authors highlight additional opportunities and strategies for advocates at the local and national level to improve educational outcomes for all AAPI students by 2040.

Introduction

In 2015, we witnessed a number of historical moments and controversies in American public education: students of color became the new majority in public schools; a movement emerged to opt students out of standardized state tests; and the long overdue reauthorization of the Elementary and Secondary Education Act (ESEA) of 1965, a fifty-year-old civil rights bill whose primary purpose is to increase educational opportunities for traditionally underserved and disadvantaged students, occurred. Against this backdrop, Asian American and Pacific Islander

(AAPI) students and advocates rallied to be recognized, seen, and heard within K–12 educational policy and the American K–12 public school system. Because of the pervasive mainstream assumption that AAPIs are academically successful and economically secure, dubbed the Asian "model minority myth," AAPI students were often not included in the national discourse that highlights disparities for students of color and seeks solutions for closing the achievement gap. As a result, AAPI advocates coalesced around obtaining more data on AAPI students and families as their primary civil rights priority in education in 2015. If the AAPI community wins the fight for transparent and available disaggregated data, by 2040 the community can move beyond dispelling the model minority myth to focus on family and student engagement in the development, funding, and implementation of K–12 education.

Demographic Changes and Masked Disparities

Fueled by the lifting of race-based immigration restrictions in the mid-1960s combined with favorable political refugee policies, the AAPI population increased tenfold between 1970 and 2010. Between 2010 and 2040, the population is expected to roughly double again. Today, AAPIs constitute 6 percent of the total U.S. population and are projected to increase to nearly 10 percent by 2040 (Ong, Ong, and Ong, 2016).

The student population within K–12 public schools reflects large demographic shifts across the United States in the last four decades. AAPI student enrollment grew fourfold from 1979 to 2009, with expected growth by another 31 percent by 2019 (Hussar and Bailey, 2013). The total share of AAPI enrollment in K–12 public schools is projected to increase to 6 percent of all enrollees over the next six years, compared to 4 percent in 1995. This means that by 2022, AAPI enrollment is estimated to reach more than three million students, compared to 1.7 million in 1997 (ibid.). These shifts are particularly significant compared to African American and Native American students, whose populations are projected to remain steady, and to white students whose enrolled populations are declining. If AAPI student enrollment continues to increase by approximately 2 percent every ten years, based on current trends in AAPI immigration, the share of AAPI student enrollment could be approximately 10 percent by 2040 (ibid.).

Looking at aggregate statistics of the AAPI student population overall, these students show remarkable academic achievement and educational attainment. AAPIs appear to be "the model minority." Compared to the overall U.S. population, AAPIs overall are better educated. A total of 85.7 percent of AAPIs have a high school diploma or higher (compared to 86.3 percent of the general population), and 50.7 percent of AAPIs have a college degree or higher (compared to 29.1 percent of the general population) (U.S. Census Bureau, 2013). Once the AAPI data is disaggregated, however, an alarming picture emerges. Stark disparities in educational attainment and economic status among AAPIs become visible.

Just as aggregated data prior to the passage of the No Child Left Behind Act masked the achievement gaps between students of color and their peers, aggregated AAPI data—which combines forty-eight ethnicities who speak more than two hundred languages into one category—masks the achievement gaps for particular subgroups within the AAPI community. Of particular note are the dramatic differences in the achievement of the Southeast Asian American and Pacific Islander groups. Examining the figures for bachelor's degree attainment or higher, it is clear that the high academic achievement of Asian Indian (70.5 percent) and Chinese Americans (52.0 percent) masks the performance of smaller ethnic groups such as Hmong (15.6 percent), Cambodian (15.5 percent), and Samoan (13.4 percent) (ibid.).

Defining the New Narrative for Educational Equity: "No Data, No Justice"

Disaggregated data on AAPI students and families is critical for ensuring educational equity and providing opportunities for disadvantaged students within the AAPI community. In K–12 public schools, federal (and often state and local) funds are allocated specifically toward closing achievement gaps. Without precise data revealing the challenges and disparities in education outcomes within the AAPI community, schools are unlikely to direct resources and interventions to better support specific struggling groups of AAPI students. As a result, AAPI data disaggregation has been identified as the primary civil rights issue in education for AAPIs.

National advocacy organizations representing the AAPI community, as well as the broader civil rights community, have embraced the idea of social justice through further data disaggregation, including AAPI data disaggregation, as a key priority for the reauthorization of the ESEA and subsequent deliberations of the final ESEA bill, the Every Student Succeeds Act (ESSA). In January 2015, more than 180 national, state, and local organizations endorsed a letter calling for AAPI data disaggregation in K–12 public schools, and more than one thousand photos were submitted by students and communities to the #AllStudentsCount campaign to show support. Respected advocacy organizations representing other communities of color, such as the Leadership Conference on Civil and Human Rights, NAACP Legal Defense Fund, the National Urban League, the League of United Latin American Citizens, and National Council of La Raza joined national AAPI advocacy organizations such as the National Council for Asian Pacific Americans, the Southeast Asia Resource Action Center, OCA—Asian Pacific American Advocates, Asian Pacific American Labor Alliance, and the Japanese American Citizens League in pushing congressional leadership to champion and support AAPI data disaggregation.

The first proposed federal legislation, the All Students Count Act, called for disaggregating AAPI data using U.S. Census categories across K–12 public schools. It was introduced in Congress in July 2014 by U.S. Representative Mike Honda (D-CA17) and then reintroduced in February 2015 with a Senate companion bill from U.S. Senator Mazie Hirono (D-HI) (Hirono, 2015; Honda, 2014, 2015). Ranking member of the Committee on Education and the Workforce U.S. Representative Bobby Scott (D-VA3) included AAPI data disaggregation using U.S. Census categories across all states in his substitute amendment to the Republican-sponsored Student Success Act. The amendment, unfortunately, did not make it to the final House bill, nor did the proposed bills from Honda and Hirono move out of their respective education committees. Nevertheless, these proposed pieces of legislation set the stage for debate and the inclusion of data disaggregation language in the long overdue reauthorization of the ESEA of 1965. With bipartisan support from U.S. Senator Dean Heller (R-NV), the Hirono-Heller amendment to the U.S. Senate ESEA bill called for AAPI data disaggregation in school districts with one thousand or more AAPI students. It was narrowly defeated 47-50 in July 2015.

Even with no language in the House or Senate ESEA bills for further disaggregating AAPI data, civil rights advocates were able to secure acknowledgment from federal policy makers on both sides of the aisle that AAPI data disaggregation is a critical issue. The final ESEA bill, the ESSA, contains conference report language that recognizes that current race and ethnicity categories "can mask particular challenges that ethnic minorities within each subgroup face. The Conferees encourage States that collect disaggregated data on ethnic minorities within individual subgroups, such as disaggregated data for Asian and Native Hawaiian/Pacific Islander students using the same race response categories as the decennial census of the population, to make such information publicly available, so long as such disclosure does not reveal any personally identifiable information for any student" (U.S. House Committee on Education and Workforce, 2015, 454). More importantly, the final ESEA bill includes statutory language for technical assistance currently offered by the U.S. Department of Education for state education agencies interested in disaggregating AAPI data and using that data to improve educational outcomes.

Importantly, interest in AAPI data disaggregation has not been limited to the federal stage. The Rhode Island General Assembly (H 5743) and the California State Legislature (AB 1088) both tried to pass data disaggregation legislation in 2011 (Diaz, Slater, and Cimini, 2011; Eng, 2011). California's bill, AB 1088, passed. It targeted the Department of Industrial Relations and Department of Fair Employment and Housing rather than education-related state agencies, but it was still a positive step forward. In 2015, another bill, AB 176, attempted to involve more state agencies (the University of California and California State University systems) in collecting disaggregated AAPI data (Bonta, 2015). AB 176 received near-unanimous support in both chambers of the California State Legislature before it was ultimately vetoed by California Governor Jerry Brown, so advocacy groups are determined to try again. Also in 2015, both New York (A02430) and Washington State (HB 1541) attempted to pass legislation asking state agencies to collect disaggregated AAPI data (Kim, 2015; Santos, Tharinger, and Orwell 2016). Advocates were successful in Washington, and on March 30, 2016, the state became the first in the nation to have a law to collect and publicly report disaggregated AAPI data. Efforts to pass AAPI data legislation continue in Minnesota, California, and Rhode Island, providing models for advocacy groups in other states where AAPI communities are concentrated.

Given the steady increase in community and bipartisan political support, legislation mandating the disaggregation of AAPI data in K–12 public schools could be enacted within the next few years. If AAPI advocates are successful by 2040, AAPI data collection, analysis, and reporting to inform student needs could be institutionalized in public elementary and secondary schools. The conversation could shift to ensuring resource equity, providing differentiated supports and interventions for specific communities, and prioritizing those identified supports. Community stakeholders may also utilize publicly available AAPI data to improve direct support services and create programs where gaps exist. Access and good use of data to improve student outcomes could also create stronger relationships between schools and the community in determining and providing appropriate supports to students and families.

Other Challenges in America's Public Schools: 2015 and 2040

A Lack of AAPI Educators

Other challenges affecting AAPIs may or may not be resolved by 2040. For example, despite dramatic shifts in student demographics over the past twelve years, teacher demographics in public schools have not shifted to match the student population. Currently, more than half of all students are students of color, but only 16.9 percent of teachers identify as teachers of color (Bristol, 2015). The current subset of these teachers who are AAPI is even smaller, at 1.4 percent, compared to the current enrollment of AAPI students at 5.2 percent (ibid.). Teacher recruitment programs must increase efforts to diversify the educator workforce in general, but ought to pay particular attention to attracting and retaining AAPI educators within the next twenty-five years. A diverse general pool of teachers trained appropriately in cultural and linguistic competency may be able to understand and address better the needs of AAPI students and communities, particularly new immigrants and refugees. However, the particular cultural and historical experiences an AAPI teacher brings to his or her teaching may provide relatable context for AAPI students that cannot simply be learned in the teacher certification and licensure process.

Bullying and Harassment

In recent years, with the popularity of racially charged stereotypes like "model minority" and "perpetual foreigner," AAPI K–12 students have increasingly suffered from bullying and violence. Limited English proficiency, economic instability, religion, and point of arrival into the country are factors that increase the likelihood of getting bullied. Bullying is defined by the federal government as "unwanted, aggressive behavior among school-aged children that involves real or perceived power imbalance where the behavior is repeated, or has the potential to be repeated, over time" (U.S. Department of Health and Human Services, 2016b). According to the U.S. Departments of Justice and Education, 54 percent of Asian American students have been bullied (Robers, Zhang, and Truman, 2010). Asian American males are also the most likely students to be bullied, more than their white, black, Native American, or Hispanic peers. This contrasts with a study conducted by the Asian American Psychological Association Leadership Fellows Program in May 2012 that found that only 17 percent of Asian American students reported being bullied, the lowest of any racial group for the same category (Tran, 2012). It is important to highlight that this data reflects the reported accounts of bullying rather than the actual incidents.

Harassment, by contrast, can "[take] many forms, including verbal acts and name-calling; graphic and written statements, which may include use of cell phones or the Internet; or other conduct that may be physically threatening, harmful, or humiliating" (Ali, 2010, 2). While Congress has no federal law directly addressing bullying (although some states and districts have adopted antibullying policies), the Office of Civil Rights is empowered by federal law to ensure students are not harassed based on their race, color, national origin, sex, or disability (U.S Department of Health and Human Services, 2016b). According to AAPI Data and the Center for American Progress, 37 percent of Asian Americans report being harassed, but for Hmong Americans it is a staggering 71 percent (Ahmad and Ramakrishnan, 2014). Filipino, Cambodian, and Vietnamese Americans are also highly likely to report being harassed.

Sikh Americans also experienced significant increases in bullying and harassment after the 9/11 terrorist attacks. Research conducted by the Sikh Coalition in Fresno, California, found that 87 percent of Sikh American students experience bullying to some degree at school (Sikh Coalition, 2014). Studies in other major cities with prominent Sikh populations found similar results. While students are generally the ones bullying their peers, teachers, administrators, and other adults have also been guilty of bullying.

In response to increased reports of bullying, some states have adopted anti-bullying policies, though each state maintains a different definition of bullying. Bullying legislation at the federal level has been introduced, though not successfully passed, and Senator Casey (D-PA) and Senator Franken (D-MN) championed the issue during the reauthorization of ESEA. Both U.S. senators have pledged to continue pushing antibullying legislation, particularly for LGBTQ students. Also, in November 2014, the Obama administration created an AAPI Bullying Prevention Task Force to address specifically the bullying of AAPI students (U.S Department of Education, 2016). In the meantime, the U.S. Department of Education can continue to address harassment by enforcing existing policy. We are hopeful that with this momentum, schools will be better equipped to address bullying, harassment, and school climate issues in general by 2040, and will be held accountable for doing so.

Language Access

Language access is critical for AAPI students and families to participate meaningfully in schools, and the U.S. Department of Education recently released guidance to mitigate language barriers in education (Lhamon and Gupta, 2015). As the student population becomes increasingly diverse, communities are beginning to demand their language access rights. For example, local community members in New Orleans lodged a civil rights complaint with the U.S. Department of Education's Office of Civil Rights about the lack of access to translators for Individualized Education Program meetings and to translated communications in both Vietnamese and Spanish to students and families in the New Orleans school district (Mariadason and Nguyen, 2013).

Changes in ESEA and the steady volume of language access cases before the U.S. Department of Justice and the U.S. Department of Education's Office of Civil Rights may force districts and schools to recognize their legal obligation to serve non-Spanish-speaking populations. In the 2013–14 academic school year, more than 161 cases involving language access were filed with the U.S. Department of Education's Office of Civil Rights (U.S. Department of Education, 2015). The current reauthorization of ESEA includes English proficiency as an indicator in state accountability systems and requires additional reporting at the state and local level on the performance of English learners. Together, these should lead to a decrease in language access violations, especially for AAPI communities, by 2040.

However, schools and districts need to work harder to engage AAPI communities (U.S. House Committee on Education and Workforce, 2015). Traditional parent organizations like the Parent Teacher Association (PTA) have low membership enrollment for AAPI parents, and to our knowledge, the PTA has never been led by an AAPI director. In response to persistently low engagement of AAPI parents and community members in education policy, SEARAC, along with other national groups, has been collecting a list of community members ready to advise policy makers as they implement the new federal education law (SEARAC, 2016).

Advocates are working to address all of these issues to improve education outcomes for AAPI students: increasing the proportion of AAPI educators, preventing bullying of AAPI students, providing appropriate language access for AAPI students and families, and empowering parents and students to engage decision makers. We are hopeful that by 2040, our students will have teachers and elected school board members who understand and share their particular cultural and historical heritage, they will feel safe in a school climate free from bullying, and their families will be able to navigate their school systems in their preferred language.

The Every Student Succeeds Act and AAPIs

A discussion on the landscape of public K–12 education would be incomplete without a brief discussion of the passage of ESSA, the reauthorization of the ESEA, and how that impacts the AAPI community. Broadly, ESSA shifts tremendous power from the federal government back to the states in a number of ways, from defining teacher effectiveness to determining what will happen when schools fail to meet the needs of traditionally underserved students. The law gives states and local districts more flexibility in their accountability plans, with the federal government no longer determining the consequences for failing schools or the interventions that will be used. In addition, states are required to "meaningfully engage" and "consult" with public stakeholders in crafting the interventions and supports that will be used to address achievement gaps for traditionally underserved students. AAPI communities potentially have the opportunity to engage schools and districts to carefully define the interventions, but must take care to understand the process and timeline for such engagement.

At the same time, ESSA also contains strong provisions for English language learners (ELLs), with ELLs now directly included in Title I state accountability plans. States must now report the English language proficiency rates of ELLs, as well as use the performance of ELLs in acquiring English proficiency as one of multiple indicators used for identifying low-performing schools that need corrective action. Combined with the new cross-tabulated reports that can examine ELLs by race and ethnicity categories, as well as disabilities, the AAPI community has the opportunity to determine whether schools and districts are meeting the specific needs of AAPI ELLs. Prior to the passage of ESSA, such data has not been consistently available to the public. Within the next few years, such data will reveal whether schools and districts have been adequately serving AAPI ELLs and whether more resources need to be targeted to specific groups of AAPI students. By 2040, longitudinal data on how schools have been serving AAPI ELLs should allow stakeholders to better advocate for supports and resources for AAPI ELLs.

ESSA also has a provision for the development of state assessments in languages other than English, which may be of interest to AAPI students and families who are recent arrivals to the United States. In its state plan, each state must identify the languages that are present to a "significant extent" within the state and indicate for which languages assessments are not available and are needed. This particular provision is part of the requirement that states include ELLs in the annual assessments, test them in a valid and reliable manner, and provide appropriate accommodations, which could include assessing in a language other than English. Technical assistance to develop such assessments in other languages is now available to states, upon request. With pressure from advocates, by 2040, each state could have assessments available in multiple languages, as AAPI languages are within the top five languages for nearly every state, with the exception of Montana and New Mexico (U.S. Department of Education, 2015).

ESSA also includes a provision for the U.S. Department of Education to provide technical assistance for state education agencies interested in disaggregating AAPI data and using that data to improve educational outcomes. This technical assistance is important for creating buy-in for states and districts that may be uncertain about the burden of implementing AAPI data disaggregation or lack the capacity to implement the changes necessary in local and state data collection processes and systems. The technical assistance is also important for states and districts that already collect disaggregated AAPI data but are unsure how to analyze and report it for program improvement. However, the AAPI community must show that there is demand for such technical assistance and AAPI data disaggregation by ensuring that districts and states take advantage of the technical assistance—or risk losing technical assistance in a future reauthorization of the ESEA. If districts and states continue to express interest in disaggregating AAPI data, the U.S. Department of Education should provide guidance documents and best practices for disaggregating AAPI data by 2040, if such practices are not already institutionalized by states and districts by then.

Challenges to Making Progress for AAPI Communities

In the last few years, substantial progress has been made in federal- and state-level policies to improve educational outcomes for AAPI students, but public stakeholders, advocates, and policy makers must be mindful that this progress is not lost. A number of challenges and obstacles may hinder or slow the trajectory toward improving educational outcomes for AAPI students through AAPI data disaggregation, targeted resources, and other supportive policies. These include, but are not limited to:

- **Shifts in the political landscape at the federal level.** The outcome of the 2016 and subsequent presidential elections may present a significant challenge to making further progress for improving the outcomes of AAPI students. The president selects the next secretary of education and has the power either to prioritize supportive education policies or to slash funding for initiatives that improve educational equity overall.

- **Multiple reauthorizations of ESEA and a new Congress.** Over the next few decades, shifts in the political balance of power in Congress may also determine whether it prioritizes meeting the needs of AAPI students and their communities. ESEA will also have to be reauthorized—and probably a few times—and each Congress may or may not include the priorities of AAPI students and families.

- **Shift in power from strong federal oversight to state flexibility.** Now that ESSA has taken power away from the federal government in favor of state flexibility, community stakeholders at the local level must be more vigilant regarding the implementation of the new law. Ensuring that services are maintained and improved will require more organization at the local level, as national civil rights organizations will not have the capacity to carefully watch implementation in all fifty states and the District of Columbia to hold state and local officials accountable. This is especially challenging for AAPI students and families, unless they have the support of strong community-based organizations or other advocacy groups carefully monitoring education programs and policies at the local and state level.

Getting There by 2040: The Next Twenty-Five Years

To further educational opportunities for all students within the diverse AAPI community, advocates and researchers must work hand in hand over the next twenty-five years to ensure that the particular priorities of AAPI communities are included in the public narrative around public education. The following recommendations address the critical need for our communities to be informed and organized to enact lasting policy change in order to ensure student success in America's public schools:

- **Setting Policy Priorities for Reauthorizing the ESEA.** In 2015, AAPI advocates set a remarkable precedent by actively collaborating with other civil rights advocates in conversations with policy makers about meeting the needs of AAPI students and families within the context of the ESEA reauthorization. ESEA is due for reauthorization at least two more times by 2040, and AAPI organizations and advocates should think proactively about what policies will further advance educational opportunities and outcomes for AAPI subgroups that still face challenges in educational attainment.

- **Passing Data Disaggregation Legislation at the State and Local Level.** As ESSA shifts more power to states, advocates are increasingly interested in passing data disaggregation legislation at the state level, and we are optimistic about enacting state legislation nationwide by 2040. With the new law that includes AAPI data disaggregation in the state of Washington, and state legislatures currently considering similar bills in California, Minnesota, and Rhode Island, the momentum for AAPI data disaggregation will grow with sustained community pressure. We recommend that advocates and researchers continue to voice demand for data disaggregation legislation, targeting districts and states with large or emerging AAPI populations. In addition, advocates can add to the momentum for nationwide policy change by showing how such data collection has been useful in increasing educational opportunities and sharing best practices. Advocates should also pressure state legislatures to adopt disaggregated data collection and reporting policies and user-friendly public disclosure of such data while ensuring student privacy.

- **Changing Teacher Preparation and Professional Development to Include Cultural and Linguistic Competency.** AAPI student enrollment is projected to be 10 percent within the next twenty-five years, based on current rates of new AAPI immigrants and refugees, many of whom have limited English proficiency (Hussar and Bailey, 2013). We recommend AAPI advocates demand that teacher preparation programs mandate cultural and linguistic competency training for all student teachers and all professional staff, including school and district administrators. At 10 percent, AAPI student enrollment rates are similar to the current enrollment rates for students with disabilities, for whom there is mandatory training in teacher preparation programs. We also recommend advocates push for the investment of additional funds for culturally and linguistically relevant professional development and training programs.

- **Amplifying the AAPI Voice in Education.** As AAPI student enrollment grows, the broader AAPI community must ensure there are sufficient advocates and organizations engaging in policy making at the local, state, and national levels, as well as offering direct services to AAPI students. We recommend advocates train parents and families to engage schools and districts in the decision-making opportunities that will emerge as ESSA is implemented. We also recommend that community advocates connect and collaborate through coalitions such as the National Council of Asian Pacific Americans. Advocates should also consider connecting with larger organizations that have AAPI initiatives, such as the Teach for America Asian American & Pacific Islander Initiative and the White House Initiative on Asian Americans and Pacific Islanders.

- **Creating Models for Educational Equity for AAPI Communities.** Some cities with high concentrations of AAPIs, like Long Beach, California, Seattle, Washington, Austin, Texas, and the Twin Cities, Minnesota, have seen the growth of language immersion schools, culturally relevant programs, and charter schools tailored to specific cultures, languages, and communities. California's first English-Vietnamese dual-language-immersion program recently opened in Orange County, California, and English-Vietnamese dual-language-immersion schools have also cropped up in cities with large Vietnamese communities in Austin, Texas, Portland, Oregon, and King County, Washington. In Minnesota, the Saint Paul Public School District has two AAPI language immersion schools, Chinese and Hmong, and offers "dual-language-immersion pathways" from elementary school through high school. Minnesota and California have also seen the emergence of charter schools that have bilingual teachers and school officials. Some of the Hmong charter schools in Minnesota even serve cultural Hmong food and integrate the Hmong language into the curriculum. There were not many language immersion schools ten years ago but the recent emergence of a handful of these schools suggests a growing trend. We anticipate more language immersion schools, especially for AAPI languages in areas where the community are strong and populous. In addition, local nonprofits like the Vietnamese Friendship Association (Seattle, Washington) and Khmer Girls in Action (Long Beach, California) partner with local schools to provide culturally relevant programming and academic services for high school students. The culturally relevant programming and partnership between schools are important for AAPI students and are present in these charter schools and language immersion schools. We recommend more funding for such programs and more partnerships between community-based organizations, schools, and school districts.

- **Working in Broad Coalitions to Further Educational Opportunity for All Students.** By 2040, one in ten Americans will be AAPIs and half of Americans will identify as a person of color. This major shift in the makeup of American society promises a shift in the current discourse about whether schools are serving specific, smaller groups of students within our public schools or whether schools are serving the majority of students within our schools. The change in demographics toward a new majority consisting of people of color is accompanied by the potential for greater political power, if broad coalitions are formed and utilized to push educational equity for all students. For AAPIs to truly advance educational opportunities for disadvantaged AAPI students, we recommend that advocates for AAPI students work hand in hand with other community groups with similar concerns to advance policies that support multiple communities. The year 2015 set a precedent at the federal level with the civil rights community advocating specifically for AAPI students and families, which resulted in greater progress overall for all students.

Conclusion

With the recent federal acknowledgment in ESEA (and ESSA) that there are disparities in educational outcomes within the diverse AAPI community, the model minority myth is well underway to being dispelled. As more and more disaggregated data comes to light—from researchers, public disclosure of currently collected data sets, and new data collections—it will be easier to pinpoint the needs of our students and families, as well as craft tailored interventions and policies to solve them. However, we cannot be complacent once the model minority myth has been dispelled, for the work will have only begun to define who we are as a community.

AAPI public stakeholders—parents, students, teachers, business owners, corporate employees, refugees, retirees, and many others—must recognize that to be included in the national discourse to improve educational opportunities for all students, we must be engaged at all levels, from the local school to the highest levels of our government. To improve language access for our students and families, we must challenge schools and agencies to provide the supports we need and file complaints with the U.S. Department of Education's Office of Civil

Rights when our rights to meaningfully participate are violated. To improve school climate, we must challenge the high rates of bullying and harassment that our students face and demand safe spaces for learning from teachers and principals, and if that fails, from those who represent us at the state and federal level. To have more AAPI educators and decision makers, we have to encourage community members to pursue the teaching profession and other positions of authority, while working with recruiters on how to better attract and support our students.

AAPI advocates, researchers, and community members must continue to mobilize and voice the desires, dreams, and demands for change to ensure that not only do all of our students count, but all of them will succeed in our public schools. Only then can we hope for educational equity by 2040.

Acknowledgments

Thank you to Kim Dang and Marcus Degnan of SEARAC for their work on the initial drafts and Mari Quenemoen of SEARAC for her editorial review and expertise.

Notes

1. Personal correspondence, from Marc Morial to author, 2014

References

Ahmad, Farah Z., and Karthick Ramakrishnan. 2014. "State of Asian Americans and Pacific Islanders Series: A Multifaceted Portrait of a Growing Population." Center for American Progress, Report. http://aapidata.com/wp-content/uploads/2015/10/AAPIData-CAP-report.pdf (accessed March 7, 2016).

Ali, Russlynn. 2010. "Dear Colleague Letter: Harassment and Bullying." U.S. Department of Education. Office for Civil Rights. 26 October. http://www2.ed.gov/about/offices/list/ocr/letters/colleague-201010.pdf (accessed March 6, 2016).

Bonta, Rob. 2015. "Data Collection." AB 176. State of California 2015–16 regular legislative session. http://leginfo.legislature.ca.gov/faces/billNavClient.xhtml?bill_id=201520160AB176 (accessed March 7, 2016).

Bristol, Travis J. 2015. "Recruiting and Retaining Educators of Color." U.S. Department of Education. White House Initiative on Educational Excellence for African Americans. Stanford Center for Opportunity Policy in Education. Webinar conducted on 7 May. http://sites.ed.gov/whieeaa/files/2014/01/Resource-Slides.pdf (accessed March 7, 2016).

Diaz, Grace, Slater, Scott, Cimini, Maria. Rhode Island Assembly Members. 2011. State of Rhode Island (H 5743), General Assembly. http://webserver.rilin.state.ri.us/BillText/BillText11/HouseText11/H5743.pdf (accessed March 7, 2016).

Eng, Mike. 2011. AB 1088. State of California 2011–12 regular legislative session. http://www.leginfo.ca.gov/pub/11-12/bill/asm/ab_1051-1100/ab_1088_bill_20111009_chaptered.html (accessed March 7, 2016).

Hirono, Mazie. 2015. "Senate Amendment 2109 to Senate Amendment 2089." S. Amdt. 2109. 114th Cong. 2015–16. https://www.congress.gov/amendment/114th-congress/senate-amendment/2109 (accessed March 7, 2016).

Honda, Mike. 2015. "All Students Count Act of 2015." H.R. 717. 114th Cong. 2015–16. https://www.congress.gov/bill/114th-congress/house-bill/717/titles (accessed March 7, 2016).

———. 2014. "All Students Count Act of 2014." H.R. 5343. 113th Cong. 2013–14. https://www.congress.gov/bill/113th-congress/house-bill/5343 (accessed March 7, 2016).

Hussar, W. J., and T. M. Bailey. 2013. *Projections of Education Statistics to 2022.* NCES 2014-051. U.S. Department of Education, National Center for Education Statistics. Washington, DC: U.S. Government Printing Office.

Kim, A. 2015. A02430A. State of New York 2015–16 regular legislative session. http://assembly.state.ny.us/leg/?default_fld=&bn=A02430&Summary=Y&Actions=Y&Text=Y&Votes=Y (accessed March 7, 2016).

Lhamon, Catherine E., and Vanita Gupta. 2015. U.S. Department of Education. Office for Civil Rights. "Dear Colleague Letter: English Learner Students and Limited English Proficient Parents." 7 January. http://www2.ed.gov/about/offices/list/ocr/letters/colleague-el-201501.pdf (accessed March 7, 2016).

Mariadason, Thomas L., and Minh Nguyen. 2013. "Re: Discrimination Against National Origin Minority Students and Parents Who are Limited English Proficient (LEP) in Orleans Parish School Board (OPSB) and Recovery School District (RSD) Schools." Asian American Legal Defense and Education Fund and Vietnamese American Young Leaders Association civil rights complaint, Letter. 2 August. http://aaldef.org/VAYLA%20AALDEF%20DOJ%20OCR%20Complaint.pdf (accessed March 7, 2016).

Ong, Jonathan, Ong, Paul, and Elena Ong. 2016. "The Future of Asian Americans in 2040." *AAPI Nexus Journal* 14(1): 14–29.

Robers, S., Zhang, J., and J. Truman. 2010. "Indicators of School Crime and Safety: 2010." NCES 2011-002/NCJ 230812. National Center for Education Statistics, U.S. Department of Education, and Bureau of Justice Statistics, Office of Justice Programs, U.S. Department of Justice. Washington, DC.

Santos, Ortiz-Self, Tharinger, Moscoso, and Gregerson Orwell. Washington State Representatives. 2016. "Implementing Strategies to Close the Educational Opportunity Gap, Based on the Recommendations of the Educational Opportunity Gap Oversight and Accountability Committee." HB 1541. State of Washington 2015–16 regular legislative session. http://apps.leg.wa.gov/billinfo/summary.aspx?bill=1541 (accessed March 7, 2016).

SEARAC. 2016. "Southeast Asian/Asian American or Pacific Islander Education Advocate (SEARAC list)." http://bit.ly/AAPIEdList (accessed March 7, 2016).

Sikh Coalition. 2014. "Go Home, Terrorist." The Sikh Coalition, Report. https://issuu.com/thesikhcoalition/docs/go-home-terrorist (accessed January 14, 2016).

Tran, Nellie. 2012. "Bullying and Victimization and Asian American Students." Asian American Psychological Association. https://www.apa.org/pi/oema/resources/ethnicity-health/asian-american/bullying-and-victimiza-tion.pdf (accessed January 14, 2016).

U.S. Census Bureau. 2013. "American Community Survey 3-Year Estimates." Tables S1501, S0201, and B15002D; American FactFinder. http://fact nder2.census.gov (accessed March 7, 2016).

U.S. Department of Education. 2016. White House Initiative on Asian Americans and Pacific Islanders. "Bullying." http://sites.ed.gov/aapi/aapi-bul-lying/ (accessed March 6, 2016).

———. Office for Civil Rights. 2015. *Protecting Civil Rights, Advancing Equity: Report to the President and Secretary of Education, Under Section 203(b)(1) of the Department of Education Organization Act, FY 13–14.* Washington, DC: U.S. Government Printing Office.

U.S Department of Health and Human Services. 2016a. "What Is Bullying: Definition." StopBullying.Gov. http://www.stopbullying.gov/what-is-bully-ing/definition/index.html (accessed March 6, 2016).

———. 2016b. "Policies and Laws: Federal Laws." StopBullying.Gov. http://www.stopbullying.gov/laws/federal/index.html (accessed March 6, 2016).

U.S. House Committee on Education and Workforce. 2015. Every Student Succeeds Act: Conference Report (to accompany S. 1177). H. Report 114-354. Washington, DC: Government Printing Office. https://www.congress.gov/114/crpt/hrpt354/CRPT-114hrpt354.pdf (accessed March 7, 2016).

RITA PIN AHRENS is Director of Education Policy at the Southeast Asia Resource Action Center and co-chair of the Education Committee for the National Council of Asian Pacific Americans. A Cambodian refugee and former math teacher, she studied psychology at Yale and earned a master's in education from the University of New Haven.

SOUVAN LEE is a Policy Associate at the Southeast Asia Resource Action Center and the son of Hmong refugees. He was a congressional page, legislative liaison, ELL teaching assistant for international graduate students, and graduate of the University of Minnesota–Twin Cities in political science.

aapi nexus Vol. 14, No. 1 (Spring 2016): 66-77

Practitioners Essay

Educational Opportunity and the Missing Minority in Higher Education:
Changing the National Narrative of Asian Americans and Pacific Islanders by 2040

Leilani Matasaua Pimentel and Neil Horikoshi

Abstract

For nearly half a century, the model minority myth has dominated perceptions of Asian American college students and masked educational disparities among the nearly fifty ethnic groups that comprise the Asian American and Pacific Islander (AAPI) communities. This essay challenges the model minority narrative by presenting the narrative of the *missing minority*—outlining how this alternative narrative was influenced by the creation of federal AAPI-serving institution legislation in 2008. The authors explore Asian American Native American Pacific Islander-Serving Institution recognition, how it has provided a framework to further support AAPI higher education outcomes, and what factors will affect the national narrative in 2040.

> When Seata Shyon isn't taking care of her siblings, she is working late into the night on homework and college applications, as she plans for her future career as a college student. She is visibly exhausted. Yet even with the dark circles under her eyes, her face betrays a quiet hope and excitement. Like many of her peers at the June Jordan School for Equity, she is working very hard so that she can be the first person in her family to go to college. Born in Samoa, Shyon, 18, and her family moved to Hawaii, before relocating to San Francisco, where they lived in public housing. When her father was incarcerated six years ago, her mother took on two jobs, leaving Shyon with the responsibility of caring for five younger siblings, including an infant (Goossen, 2009, 1).

Introduction

Since the 1960s, the model minority myth has depicted Asian American students as beacons of academic success. In the 1980s, national publications such as *Newsweek*, *Time*, and *Fortune* featured prominent articles praising and publicizing the successes of Asian American students. In recent decades, however, portrayals of "Those Asian American Whiz Kids," such as in *Time*'s 1987 feature cover, have evolved into sayings far more cynical than praiseworthy: "MIT stands for Made in Taiwan" and "UCLA stands for United Caucasians Lost among Asians."

Having permeated the national discourse on Asian Americans—and the broader Asian American and Pacific Islander (AAPI) community—the model minority narrative has overshadowed an alternate and more realistic narrative: that AAPIs are a *missing minority* in higher education. This missing minority narrative tells a story similar to those of most minority communities: high poverty rates, low educational outcomes, and lack of access to higher education. It is the story of students like Seata, a Samoan American and Vietnamese American student from San Francisco balancing family responsibilities beyond those of an average American high school student with college applications. However, unlike other minority communities, this story is both ignored and perpetuated by America's widely held misconception that all AAPIs are whiz kids.

In contrast to the model minority narrative, the AAPI community represents varying degrees of educational access and socioeconomic status. With such a vast range of demographic characteristics, the AAPI community is also the fastest-growing racial group in America. Over the next decade, AAPI college enrollment is projected to increase by 35 percent and to grow significantly more by the year 2040, when one out of ten Americans will be of Asian American or Pacific Islander descent (Ong and Ong, 2015; CARE and APIASF, 2013).

Only in the last decade has the missing minority narrative of AAPIs surfaced in the realm of higher education policy with the creation of the Asian American Native American Pacific Islander-Serving Institution (AANAPISI) federal grant program. But while the AANAPISI designation and its grant programs for AAPI-serving institutions represent a measure of success, what will it take to continue these efforts into the future? As the AAPI community continues to grow at a rate faster than any other racial group over the next quarter century, the prevailing narrative—either the perpetuation of the model minority or the revelation of the missing minority narrative—will inevitably drive higher education policy. The factors contributing to these narratives therefore demand attention as we look to the future. In this article we will explore AANAPISI recognition, how it has provided a framework to further support AAPI higher education outcomes, and what factors will affect the national narrative in 2040.

AANAPISIs as a Possible Solution to Contesting the Model Minority Myth

Representing nearly fifty distinct ethnicities and more than three hundred spoken languages, AAPIs have also become the fastest-growing poverty population in America following the recent recession. According to poverty data from the U.S. Census, the number of AAPIs living below poverty increased by more than half a million from 2007 to 2011, representing a 38 percent increase for all AAPIs (37 percent for Asian Americans and 60 percent for Pacific Islanders). Nearly 60 percent of the increase of AAPI poor consisted of the native-born segment of the population, and U.S. Census data point to many communities including Cambodian, Hmong, and Marshallese experiencing poverty rates that are more than double the national average (CARE and APIASF, 2013). Furthermore, the significant growth rate of AAPI poor is not reflected in the population's overall poverty rate (12.8 percent in 2000, 13.1 percent in 2011) due to the rapidly growing base of AAPIs and large numbers of highly skilled, highly educated immigrants.

Despite these realities, the AAPI community has historically been distanced from America's definition of "minority." Minority-serving institutions (MSIs), postsecondary institutions that provide access to and serve the needs of low-income, underrepresented students of color, have received special federal recognition for decades. However, institutions serving high proportions of AAPIs in the United States have been excluded from federal MSI designation until recently. While hundreds of millions of dollars have been available to institutions that support historically black colleges and universities (HBCUs), tribal colleges and universities, and Hispanic-serving institutions (HSIs), not until the last decade did AAPI leaders begin to gain steam in their efforts to advocate for greater resources for underprivileged AAPI students and families.

Park and Teranishi (2008) date the push for MSI designation to the late 1990s. They note that in 1999, a College Board report entitled "Reaching the Top, the College Boards' National Task Force on Minority High Achievement," which grouped Asian Americans with whites in terms of educational achievement, served as a catalyst for AAPI advocates who sought to draw attention to the low educational outcomes of underserved ethnic groups such as Southeast Asians and Pacific Islanders. In 2001, the White House Initiative on Asian Americans and Pacific Islanders recommended a new federal designation for institutions serving significant percentages of AAPI students (Conrad and Gasman, 2015; Park and Teranishi, 2008).

In 2002, Congressman Robert Underwood (D-Guam) introduced H.R. 4825, an amendment to Title III of the Higher Education Act of 1965. Years later, and with efforts by Congressman David Wu (D-OR), Senator Barbara Boxer (D-CA), and Senator Daniel Akaka (D-HI), the U.S. Congress authorized AAPI-serving institutions with the College Cost Reduction and Access Act of 2007 and the Higher Education Opportunity Act of 2008 according to the U.S. Department of Education.

AANAPISI federal designation was enacted into law as a means of enabling institutions to improve and expand their capacity to serve AAPIs and low-income individuals. According to the legislation, institutions of higher education could be eligible to receive funds if they had an enrollment of at least 10 percent AAPI college students and at least 50 percent of degree-seeking students receiving financial assistance in at least one of the following federal programs: Federal Pell Grant, Federal Supplemental Educational Opportunity Grant, Federal Work Study, or the Federal Perkins Loan. The first grantees of fiscal year 2008 included six institutions of higher education from Maryland, Washington, California, Hawai'i, and Guam.

In *Understanding Minority-Serving Institutions* Julie Park and Robert Teranishi explore AAPI-serving institution legislation as a *racial project*—seeking to "reinterpret racial dynamics by challenging the model minority image and carving out a unique space for Asian Americans in the racial spectrum" (Park and Teranishi, 2008, pp.112). In this regard, AANAPISI recognition could be viewed as the AAPI community's first tangible victory in its mission to reassert the AAPI needs with minority needs and thereby advocate for underserved AAPI students.

Sharing Experiences of Low-Income AAPI Students through AANAPISI Research

Building on the momentum of AANAPISI designation and the growing need for research on AAPI higher education issues, the Asian and Pacific Islander American Scholarship Fund (APIASF) and the National Commission on Asian American and Pacific Islander Research in Education (CARE) issued a series of research papers beginning in 2008. Among the findings of the series of the CARE reports were disparities in educational attainment among AAPI ethnic groups, the rapid increase in AAPI students attending community colleges, contrasts between the AAPI students attending four-year institutions and those attending community colleges, and the impact of AANAPISI programs on student success.

For example, while more than 80 percent of East Asians (Chinese, Japanese, and Korean) and South Asians (Asian Indian and Pakistani) who enrolled in college earned at least a bachelor's degree, high numbers of other AAPI ethnic groups are enrolling in college but failing to earn a degree. Among Southeast Asians, 33.7 percent of Vietnamese, 42.9 percent of Cambodians, 46.5 percent of Laotians, and 47.5 percent of Hmong adults (twenty-five years or older) reported having attended college but not earning a degree. Among Pacific Islanders, the proportions are even higher with 47 percent of Guamanians, 50 percent of Native Hawaiians, 54 percent of Tongans, and 58 percent of Samoans entering college but not earning a degree (CARE, 2011). Between 50 percent and 60 percent of Pacific Islanders and between 50 percent and 65 percent of South East Asians ages twenty-five through thirty-four report having not attended college at all (CARE and APIASF, 2014).

In its 2010 and 2011 reports, CARE also identified a growing prevalence of AAPIs in community colleges, providing contrast to the widespread assumptions that all Asian American students attend prestigious four-year universities. The reports identified a 73.3 percent increase in AAPI community college enrollment between 1990 and 2000 compared to a 42.2 percent increase in public four-year institutions (CARE, 2010). Furthermore, nearly 50 percent of AAPIs are enrolled in community college.

Even more compelling are the disparities between AAPI students enrolled at two-year institutions and four-year institutions with respect to risk factors such as delayed enrollment, lack of a high school diploma, part-time enrollment, having dependents other than a spouse, single-parent status, and working full-time while enrolled. From 2003 to 2004, 74.7 percent of AAPI students at two-year institutions reported one or more risk factors while 77.3 percent of AAPI students at four-year institutions reported no risk factors at all. AAPI community college students were also more likely to enter college with lower levels of academic preparation in English and mathematics. Furthermore, 55.2 percent of AAPI students entering two-year institutions had never taken a math course beyond Algebra II in high school, compared to only 12.7 percent of AAPI students entering four-year institutions in that same year.

CARE's most recent report, "The Impact of Scholarships for Asian American and Pacific Islander Community College Students," found that AAPI community college students also have a high rate of immigrant-origin backgrounds. More than 80 percent of participants were either immigrants or children of immigrants—a figure three times higher than the percentage of immigrant-origin community college students as a whole (24 percent). CARE also found that a high proportion of AAPI community college students are first-generation college students with 82.6 percent of participants having parents who never attended college, which is also much higher than the national average for all community college students (36 percent). Additionally, 78.7 percent of AAPI students reported family responsibilities interfered with their academics.

Factors Affecting the 2040 Narrative

Not even a decade since official recognition by the federal government, the federal AANAPISI program plays a critical role in the success of AAPI students in higher education by providing funding to support institutional capacity building, curriculum development, faculty training, data collection, leadership development, academic resources, and programs that support student retention and graduation at a local level. However, additional funding for the AANAPISI program and support of AAPI students through other resources, effective data, and holistic policies taking into account the diversity of the AAPI community will greatly impact the AAPI narrative in 2040.

Federal Funding

A 2013 Partnership for Equity in Education through Research study in collaboration with CARE and APIASF also highlighted the impact of AANAPISI-funded programs on AAPI student success and persistence based on key factors including institutional culture, responsiveness to students, student connection with AANAPISI-funded staff, community engagement, and leadership development. However, the study also found that there is great need for further investment and capacity building for emerging AANAPISIs.

As a relatively new federal designation in comparison to other MSIs such as HBCUs and HSIs, AANAPISIs continue to be largely unknown even among higher education and policy leaders. AANAPISIs could benefit from capacity building that ultimately supports further research, advocacy, and contact between institutions. Without such support, AANAPISIs continue to be disconnected from opportunities that should be available to all MSIs and are challenged in their ability to share publicly the impact of their programs.

Following the passage of the Higher Education Opportunity Act, there were 116 AANAPISI-eligible institutions nationwide by 2009 according to campus data on AAPI and low-income students. The number then grew to 148 institutions in 2011 (CARE, 2011) and 153 institutions by June 2013 (CARE and APIASF, 2014). Of the 153 eligible institutions nationwide at the time of the study, only seventy-eight (51 percent) had applied for and received formal AANAPISI designation. Of the seventy-eight designated AANAPISIs, only twenty-one (14 percent) applied for and received funding. Furthermore, while the 153 eligible AANAPISIs supported 41 percent of all AAPI students attending any postsecondary institution in the country, they represented only 3 percent of all postsecondary institutions in the country (ibid.). This alarming statistic illustrates the high concentration of AAPI students in just a few campuses and communities in the United States, primarily in California, New York, and Hawai'i, along with communities in Georgia, Illinois, and Texas—areas that historically have not had a high proportion of AAPIs.

According to a recent report issued by the Congressional Research Service, there are currently 172 institutions eligible for AANAPISI designation. However, to date, only twenty-seven AANAPISIs have applied for and received funding through the federal AANAPISI program. According to the most recently posted application for MSI grants in the Federal Register for fiscal year 2016 awards, HSIs had an estimated available funding total of $52,287,473 with an estimated range of awards at $500,000 to $650,000 per campus, whereas AANAPISIs were given an estimated $3,062,000, with $200,000 to $300,000 per year estimated for each campus.

Given the limited resources from the federal government for the AANAPISI program, which is also structured as a competitive grant process, institutions will certainly be limited in the amount of federal resources they are able to secure. With the growing AAPI population over the next few decades, it is vital to AAPI student success that federal funding for the program continue through and beyond 2040.

Data-Driven Advocacy

Population projections show the number of Asian American registered voters will double to about twelve million in 2040. Furthermore, among Asian American voters, U.S.-born voters will also account for majority of the net increase (Ong and Ong, 2015) and their median age will be thirty-seven years old, meaning that the future makeup of the Asian American electorate will be increasingly more U.S.-born, younger, and potentially also more connected to AAPI issues in higher education. Given population projections and expected demographic shifts by 2040, it is crucial that AAPI leaders and organizations continue to engage AAPI citizens and build coalitions to advocate for AAPI policy issues and further investment in AANAPISIs.

But in order to advocate more effectively, robust data must be available. Data on certain ethnic groups within the AAPI community reflect the widely held belief that all AAPIs come from highly educated families, whereas the lack of data on smaller, less visible ethnic groups mask the stark reality that AAPIs also have some of the highest poverty rates in the nation. Largely invisible subethnicities within the AAPI label, such as Pacific Islanders and Southeast Asians, are often excluded from the national education dialogue and policy decisions. The unique needs of newly arrived refugee groups, who also tend not to identify as "Asian American," are also blurred by the larger AAPI label and mainstream misconceptions.

Data disaggregation based on ethnicity has been a major issue of the AAPI community and several attempts to pass legislation to change federal policy are still underway. However, even if change on a national level may be years ahead of us, we must advocate for change locally and within each campus, and particularly within large state systems supporting a high proportions of AAPIs. Considering the diverse needs of the AAPI community, it is crucial that the community, as a whole, continues to support a diverse array of interventions targeted to specific ethnic groups and regions.

While AANAPISI legislation provided an impetus to increase awareness that AAPI issues were missing from discussions on minority student achievement, these findings and the opportunity to share them with leading decision makers in the government, federal, and nonprofit sectors have served as part of a growing effort to not only raise the banner of the missing minority narrative but to also activate support and action among key stakeholders. America's demography is changing and in order to thrive, policy makers must respond by disaggregating the data for the problem and solution and developing skilled and effective leadership within AAPI communities.

Multiraciality

The issue of multiraciality will also likely affect the supply of AANA-PISIs should a greater number of multiracial students enroll in institutions that would be considered AANAPISI designated. Current 2015 to 2040 projections highlight a growth rate of 104 percent multiracial Asians overall and 130 percent of the adult population (Ong and Ong, 2015). In fact, growing numbers of multiracial AAPIs may eventually diminish the supply of AANAPISIs simply due to the fact that current national data collection methods are not favorable toward the multiracial AAPI student count.

Currently, the National Center for Education Statistics (U.S. Department of Education, 2013) collects race and ethnicity data and reports to the Integrated Postsecondary Education Data System through the following guidelines. If the individual self-identifies as "Hispanic only or Hispanic and any race category," they are reported as "Hispanic." If the individual self-identifies as "Not Hispanic; Asian only" or "Not Hispanic; Native Hawaiian or Other Pacific Islander only," they are reported as "Asian" or "Native Hawaiian or Other Pacific Islander," respectively. If the individual self-identifies as "Not Hispanic; more than one race category," they are reported as "two or more races." As a result, only students who report being Asian or Native Hawaiian or Other Pacific Islander *alone* are counted toward the 10 percent threshold for AANAPISI designation. Given the projected increase of multiracial Asian Americans, it is crucial that policy reflect the changing demographics.

Available Funding for Race-Conscious and Income-Based Scholarships

Scholarships for underrepresented students, such as racial or ethnic minorities, should be inclusive of low-income AAPI students. Scholarships for low-income AAPI students provide support for access, persistence, and success amidst key risk factors. These students, especially in community college settings, face a number of challenges that are often overlooked, masked by aggregate data, or misunderstood. For example, CARE's 2015 report found that 41.7 percent of AAPI community college students indicated that work interfered with their studies every week. Students reported forgoing studying (60.7 percent), being late to class (24.9 percent), missing class (16.6 percent), and dropping a class because of work (7.1 percent). Of the students in this study who were employed, 43.4 percent worked forty hours or more per week, which is higher than the national average of 32.4 percent for all community college students. In an earlier report, CARE also found that AAPI college students are three times more likely to have considered leaving college for nonacademic reasons than AAPI students with parents who had attended college (33.8 percent vs. 11.5 percent).

However, 81.1 percent of students indicated that the financial aid they receive directly impact their ability to succeed in college. Scholarships also affected academic outcomes including the rate of credit accumulation to make steady progress toward earning a degree or transferring to a four-year institution. Receiving a scholarship was associated with improvements in academic success and educational expectations and decreased the number of hours worked.

Conclusion

As the AAPI community continues to grow at a rate faster than any other racial group over the next quarter of a century, Asian Americans and Native Hawaiians and Pacific Islanders will continue to be among the fastest growing racial groups in America; but as this occurs, AAPIs will remain among the most diverse, and most misunderstood, groups in America.

Given the increased number of AAPIs who experienced poverty in the United States over the past decade, the anticipated 35 percent growth of AAPI students enrolling in college over the next decade, and the anticipated growth of AAPI students who will need to enroll in, and complete, college by 2040 when college completion and/or advanced degree completion becomes the "new normal," attention must be paid to the AAPI student population in order to effectively support their educational, professional, and personal success.

The changing demography, federal funding, data collection standards, and the availability of resources to help AAPI access higher education and persist through graduation will play a significant role in shaping the AAPI higher education narrative. Moreover, this narrative—along with advocacy efforts and supporting data—will shape policies affecting one in ten of the U.S. population by 2040. Looking ahead at 2040, it is paramount that the narrative of AAPI students are not left missing in the shadow of the model minority.

The successful efforts of those trying to raise awareness of and support for the diverse needs of AAPIs in higher education in the future will significantly depend upon on our success in addressing the country's perception of AAPI students in the present. By 2040, will the mainstream narrative of model minorities remain? Or will the narrative of a missing minority lacking access to educational opportunity come to the forefront? Will the publicized successes of certain segments of the AAPI population overshadow the support needed in low-income AAPI communities? Or will the successes and hopeful stories of first-generation AAPI college graduates finally change the national narrative?

To all students and scholars, college really is an option, not just a dream.

Seata Shyon, Education and Social Policy Research Assistant, APIASF 2009 Scholar, and 2013 Smith College Graduate

Acknowledgments

We thank APIASF 2009 Scholar, Seataoaifalenaoti "Seata" Shyon, for generously sharing her story and experience as an AAPI first-generation college graduate.

References

Conrad, C., and M. Gasman. 2015. *Educating a Diverse Nation: Lessons from Minority-Serving Institutions.* Cambridge, MA: Harvard University Press.

Goossen, Carolyn. 2009. "High Hopes for College Despite Low Test Scores." *New Media,* 10 February.

Ong, Paul and Elena Ong. 2015. "The Future of Asian America in 2040: Asian American Electorate to Double." UCLA Center for the Study of Inequality and Asian Pacific American Institute for Congressional Studies. http://luskin.ucla.edu/sites/default/files/AA2040_report.pdf (accessed April 5, 2016).

National Commission on Asian American and Pacific Islander Research in Education (CARE). 2011. *The Relevance of Asian Americans and Pacific Islanders in the College Completion Agenda.* New York, NY.

————.2010. *Federal Higher Education Policy Priorities and the Asian American and Pacific Islander Community.* New York, NY.

National Commission on Asian American and Pacific Islander Research in Education (CARE), and Asian & Pacific Islander American Scholarship Fund (APIASF). 2015. *The Impact of Scholarships for Asian American and Pacific Islander Community College Students: Findings from an Experimental Design Study.* New York, NY.

————.2014. *Measuring the Impact of MSI-Funded Programs on Student Success.* New York, NY.

————.2013. *Partnership for Equity in Education through Research (PEER): Findings from the First Year of Research on AAANAPISIs.* New York, NY.

Park, J. J., and R. T. Teranishi. 2008. "Asian American and Pacific Islander Serving Institutions: Historical Perspectives and Future Prospects." Pp. 111–126 in *Understanding Minority-Serving Institutions,* ed. M. Gasman, B. Baez, and C. S. Turner. Albany, NY: SUNY Press.

U.S. Department of Education, National Center for Education Statistics. 2013. *Total Fall Enrollment in Degree-Granting Postsecondary Institutions, by Level of Enrollment, Sex, Attendance Status, and Race/Ethnicity of Student: Selected Years, 1976 through 2012.* Washington, DC: Digest of Education Statistics.

LEILANI MATASAUA PIMENTEL, Development Manager, Strategic Initiatives joined APIASF in 2015 from Capitol Hill where she managed higher education and AAPI policy issues for Congressman Eni Faleomavaega (American Samoa). At APIASF, Leilani oversees partnerships with foundations, government, corporations, and community stakeholders to support access, persistence, and success for underserved AAPI students. Leilani graduated with a bachelor's degree in urban studies from Stanford University where she also conducted research for the *Stanford Social Innovation Review* and received two fellowships from the Haas Center for Public Service to support education access in low-income communities. She is currently pursuing postgraduate studies at Georgetown University's McCourt School of Public Policy.

NEIL HORIKOSHI, President and Executive Director joined APIASF in 2008 after a distinguished thirty-year career at International Business Machines Corporation, where he served in legal and executive management positions in the United States and Asia Pacific. Through his leadership, APIASF has formed strategic partnerships with AANAPISIs, expanded organizational programming to better meet the needs of underserved AAPI students, and received national recognition as a socially impactful organization. Neil graduated from the University of Hawai'i, Manoa with a bachelor's degree in business administration, and received his JD and MBA from the University of Southern California.

aapi nexus Vol. 14, No. 1 (Spring 2016): 78-96

Practitioners Essay

Asian American Workers and Unions:
Current and Future Opportunities for Organizing Asian American and Pacific Islander Workers

Johanna Hester, Kim Geron,
Tracy Lai, and Paul M. Ong

Abstract

The purpose of this essay is to explore the current and future potential for engaging Asian Americans and Pacific Islanders (AAPIs) in the labor movement by 2040. Because of the limitations of the data and the scope of the projections, we initially analyze Asian American participation in the labor market, so we can later discuss our vision and trajectory for engaging AAPI workers in the labor movement by 2040.

Introduction

Asian Americans are the fastest-growing racial population in America and the fastest-growing racial segment of America's labor market. Asian Americans have played, and will continue to play, an increasingly vital role in the U.S. economy and in organized labor.

According to the U.S. Bureau of Labor Statistics, the Asian American civil labor force grew 61 percent, from 5.5 million to 8.8 million between 1994 and 2014. Over the next decade, it is projected to grow another 23 percent, to 10.8 million, by 2024 and even higher by 2040. By 2024, the Asian American civil labor force will comprise 6.6 percent of America's workforce, up from 4.2 percent in 1994 (U.S. Bureau of Labor Statistics, 2015). It is anticipated that the proportion of Asian Americans in the labor market will be even higher by 2040.

Overall, Asian American workers appear to be doing relatively well compared to non-Hispanic whites (NHWs). However, ample statistical averages mask significant internal differences. The Asian American labor market is bifurcated—Asian American workers are overrepresented at the lower and the higher ends of the labor market. There has also been a rise in the distribution of Asian Americans in the labor market. Disparities in human capital (e.g., education and language ability) and the gender gap contribute to the relative earnings inequality.

Unions play a critically important role in giving workers a collective voice when it comes to negotiating compensation, benefits, and employment conditions. Unions are effective in mitigating downward pressure on wages and creating a more leveled playing field. Union membership is attractive to workers who would like an organization to represent, voice, and negotiate their interests.

Throughout the course of history, unions have not always had an amicable relationship with Asian Americans because new Asian immigrants have been hired to break labor strikes as scab labor. Also, anti-Asian union leaders racialized economic fears by white workers.[1] Over time, this relationship has changed because of the growth of Asian Americans in industries targeted by unions. Since the 1990s, Asian Americans played a more significant leadership role, and the absolute and relative size of Asian American union membership has increased, amidst an overall decline in unionism. In fact, between 2003 and 2009, Asian American workers were among the fastest-growing racial group in the union workforce (Rho et al, 2011). The increase is also related to two other factors: first, a shift in AFL-CIO policy to support concerted efforts to organized immigrant labor regardless of legal status and, second, ethnic mobilization and activism within the Asian American and Latino communities.

Despite these gains more could be done because, in recent years, the nonunionized segment of the Asian American labor force has grown faster than the unionized segment. As we look toward the future, unions could take a number of actions to increase financial benefits, security, and labor wins that could further increase, empower, and embolden Asian American union participation.

Current Status

Over the last decade, Asian Americans have become an increasingly important component of the U.S. labor force. Just like the overall rapid growth of the Asian American population, the Asian American labor force has grown extremely fast, faster than any other major racial group (see Figure 1). Between 2004 and 2014, the nation's labor force grew by 5.8 percent. While the number of NHW workers declined by 2.5 percent, there was a 13.4 percent growth among African Americans, a 31.6 percent growth among Hispanics, and a 39.7 percent growth among

Asian Americans. Because of the differential growth, Asian Americans increased from 4.3 percent to 5.6 percent of the labor force. Even more remarkable is the fact that Asian Americans accounted for more than a quarter (29 percent) of the net increase in the U.S. labor force.

Figure 1. Growth Rate of Labor Force: 2004–14

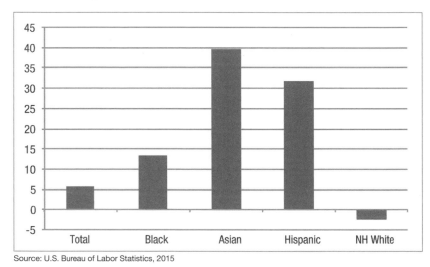

Source: U.S. Bureau of Labor Statistics, 2015

Table 1. Labor Market Status of Asian Americans, 2011–13

United States	Asian American	NH White
Labor Market Indicators		
Civilian Labor Force Participation	65.1%	62.9%
Unemployment	7.1%	7.6%
Selected Occupations		
Management, Business, etc.	49.3%	40.4%
Sales, Office, etc.	20.7%	25.0%
FT/FY Earnings		
With FT/FY Employment	71.4%	70.1%
Mean Amount (weighted average)	$69,265	$64,077

Source: U.S. Census Bureau, American Fact Finder, 2011–13 American Community Survey

Table 1 compares the labor market status of Asian Americans (alone and mixed race) relative to NHWs using standard indicators.[2] Table 1 suggests that Asian Americans are doing better than their NHW counterparts. It suggests that Asian Americans have higher participation rates and lower joblessness, and are more likely to be in managerial occupations. It suggests that Asian Americans are more likely to be fully employed and earn more, although this is partly offset by their disproportionate concentration in high-cost, large metropolitan areas (e.g., the San Francisco Bay Area, Southern California, Honolulu, New York City, and Seattle). Many of these labor market outcomes may be due to higher educational attainment (more than half of Asian American adults have at least a bachelor's degree, compared with about a third for NHW adults). In addition, higher education among Asian Americans is rooted in the biases in immigration policies and regulations that favor the highly skilled workers and their relatives.

Economic Disparities

Looking at the aggregate statistics paints a portrait of Asian Americans as a model minority—financially secure and economically mobile. In order to capture the barriers facing this group, as well as vast distinctions among them, it is important to disaggregate the data. Once we do, we find that Asian American workers continue to face discrimination despite their educational achievements. "Asians earn less than white Americans who are similar in terms of education level, work experience, geographical distribution and other characteristics" compared with foreign-born Asians who are more likely to face discrimination and wage gaps because of their race than U.S.-born (Kim, 2011, 63). The existence of a bamboo ceiling for Asian Americans is also well documented. While Asian Americans are able to obtain professional jobs because of their higher education levels, they are less likely than white Americans to advance to higher-level management positions (Kim and Mar, 2007). As one study found, when controlling for field of study, college type, region of residence, and other demographic variables, Asian American "college educated women suffer some kind of disadvantage, regardless of their nativity and immigration status" with Asian immigrants without U.S. educational credentials suffering the most (Kim and Zhao, 2014, p. 642).

The "model minority" stereotype also fails to capture the heterogeneity in employment outcomes, which are driven by differences in human capital and circumstances (see Table 2). Immigrants comprise a large majority of the Asian American working-age population, so employment outcomes are also related to English language ability, cultural barriers, and years in the United States. Many political refugees from war-torn countries also face additional hurdles in the form of posttraumatic stress disorder. Asian Americans are only a third as likely to be

U.S.-born, and, among the foreign-born, Asian Americans are more likely to be newer immigrants. Asian Americans are also twenty times more likely to not speak English well. While Asian Americans are more likely to have a college degree, they are also more likely to not have a high school degree.

Table 2. Human Capital Indicators

	Asian American	NH White
Nativity		
% U.S.-Born Among Immigrants	33.6%	96.1%
% Established Immigrants (arrived pre-2000)	59.9%	69.2%
% Newer Immigrants (arrived 2000 and after)	40.1%	30.8%
English Language Ability		
% Less Than Well	35.1%	1.6%
Educational Attainment		
% with Less Than High School	14.3%	8.6%
% with Bachelor's or Higher	50.7%	32.5%

Source: U.S. Census Bureau, American Fact Finder, 2011–13 American Community Survey

There is a relatively higher degree of inequality among Asian American workers relative to NHW men. This can be seen in Figure 2, which compares relative distributions for full-time and full-year (FT/FY) workers.

Figure 2. Asian-to-White Earnings Ratio

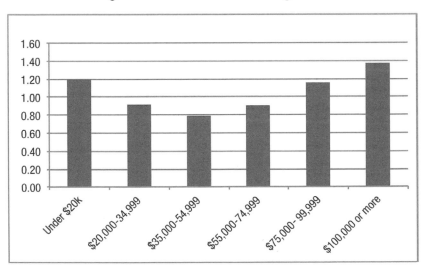

Source: U.S. Census Bureau, American FactFinder, 2011–13 American Community Survey

The points on the graph are parity indices that report whether Asian Americans are underrepresented (value less than 1) or overrepresented (value greater than 1) for each of the FT/FY earnings categories. Asian Americans are overrepresented among the lowest earners (under $20,000 per year). Asian American women are underrepresented among those in the two highest earnings ranges. The overall results illustrate that Asian American workers are relatively bifurcated, overrepresented at both the top and bottom end.

Income heterogeneity is correlated with ethnicity. There are systematic differences in human capital and other factors discussed earlier. In 2008–10, 52 percent of Asian Americans who were twenty-five years of age and older had a bachelor's degree or higher compared to just 29 percent of non-Asians. Of the Asian groups, Asian Indians had the highest rate with 75 percent, followed by Koreans with 56.3 percent, then Chinese with 53.4 percent having achieved a bachelor's degree or higher (Allard, 2011). In contrast, only about 30 percent of Vietnamese Americans earned this level of education.

Table 3 provides additional information on the ethnic disparities along key factors that affect labor market outcomes. Not surprisingly, immigrants and those with limited English language ability comprise a disproportionately higher share of the groups with less education. The Southeast Asian refugee populations are particularly disadvantaged.

Table 3. Asian Ethnic Differences

	% Foreign-born	% Speak English Less Than "Very Well"	% with Less Than High School Diploma	% with Bachelor's or Higher
Asian Indian	71.3%	20.9%	8.4%	72.1%
Bangladeshi	73.6%	44.5%	16.8%	48.2%
Cambodian	58.6%	41.3%	35.2%	15.2%
Chinese	69.2%	45.9%	18.4%	52.8%
Filipino	65.8%	22.4%	7.5%	48.0%
Hmong	39.9%	38.1%	32.8%	15.6%
Japanese	39.4%	23.0%	4.9%	48.6%
Korean	73.2%	43.7%	7.7%	53.5%
Laotian	57.3%	39.2%	31.2%	12.3%
Pakistani	65.8%	27.7%	12.9%	54.2%
Vietnamese	67.3%	52.1%	28.9%	26.3%

Source: Compiled by Paul Ong, 2011–13 American Community Survey

The economic consequences of these systematic ethnic differences are evident in Figure 3. The group with the lowest annual mean FT/FY earnings earned only forty cents for every dollar earned by the group with the highest annual mean earnings.

Figure 3. 2011–13 FT/FY Annual Mean Earnings

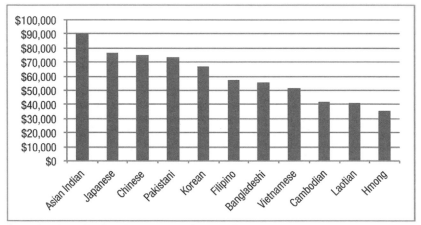

Source: Compiled by Paul Ong, 2011–13 American Community Survey

Figure 4. 2011–13 Parity Index, Relative to Non-Hispanic White Men

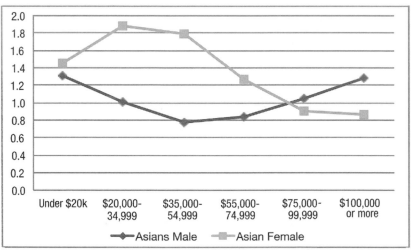

Source: Bureau of Labor Statistics, 2011–13

Comparing averages, as noted before, obscures within-group heterogeneity, and this is true in the case of the impact of gender and race.

Figure 4 reanalyzes the parity analysis discussed earlier, this time by gender. Relative to NHW men, both Asian American men and women are overrepresented among the lowest earners (less than $20,000 per year), as well as the next two categories. In contrast, while Asian men are overrepresented in the two highest earnings ranges, Asian women are underrepresented in these ranges. Overall, the results reveal that Asian American women fare worse than Asian American men, in part due to gender discrimination and inequality. Thus, gender also matters.

Gender

Men have higher labor force participation rates. But, Asian women are twice as likely to work part-time (21 percent vs. 10 percent) (Allard, 2011, 11). Similarly, while Asian men and women have similar rates in the management business occupations and educational attainment, women earn less. The median FT/FY earnings for Asian American women is only 80.4 percent of the median FT/FY earnings for Asian American men. Figure 5 illustrates that Asian American and Pacific Islander (AAPI) women earn 75 percent of what AAPI men earn (Shiu, 2014).

Figure 5. Women's Pay Gap by Race and Ethnicity (weekly earnings of women as percent of men of same race)

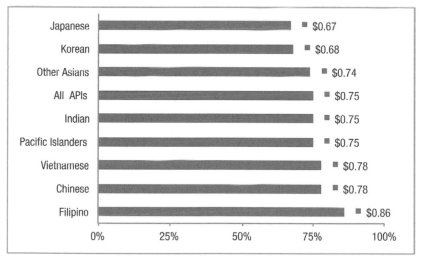

Source: Council of Economic Advisors, calculations from Bureau of Labor Statistics, and Current Population Survey

Asian American Unionism

Over the last fifteen to twenty-five years, the absolute and relative Asian American union membership has increased, partially offsetting an overall decline in unionism (see Figure 5 and also Schmitt and Warner, 2010; Schmitt, Rho, and Woo, 2011). During this time period, Asian American union membership increased 45 percent from 545,000 in 2000 to 788,000 by 2015, while total union membership declined by 9.4 percent, from 16.3 million to 14.8 million. At the same time, Asian Americans became a growing proportion of unionized workers, rising from 3 percent of all union workers in 1989 to 5 percent in 2009. Asian Americans are concentrated in sectors, such as the public sector, which has a 35.2 percent unionization rate (Buckner, 2016). Also, as illustrated in Figure 6, and as discussed previously, Asian American numbers have grown in the workforce, which has led to a growth in their union density.

Figure 6. Union Membership

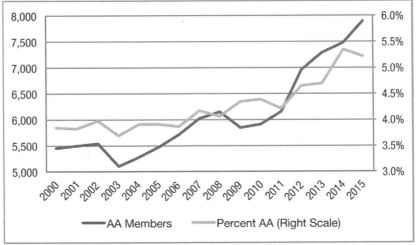

Source: Bureau of Labor Statistics, 2000–15

Union membership increases wages and benefits. Among Asian American workers with similar age, gender, education, location, and industry, union membership increases wages and benefits, particularly among the lowest paid workers. As illustrated in Figure 7, Asian American wage earners in jobs with union contracts earn 14 percent more than nonunion workers. Among the fifteen lowest paid occupations, unionized workers earned 20 percent more than Asian American workers in similar nonunionized jobs and are more likely to have health insurance benefits and a retirement plan (Schmitt, Rho, and Woo, 2011). Many of these benefits were at risk in 2015 when both public- and private-sector employers sought to reduce labor costs. That is why it was essential for unionized workers to defend worker's rights and be unified in the effort to raise the minimum wage to $15 in 2015. Unionized Asian American workers were more likely to have health insurance and a retirement plan than nonunionized workers (ibid.).

Figure 7. Union versus Nonunion Wages

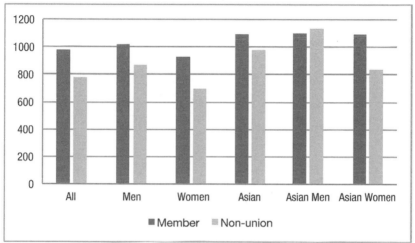

Source: Bureau of Labor Statistics, 2014–15

Union wages are better for all workers and all Asians, and for Asian American women, in particular (but less so for Asian American men). Benefits alone are not all it takes to increase Asian American unionism. It is also about political will. For example, Asian American participation has been due to a number of factors over the past fifteen to twenty-five years. The first is a shift in AFL-CIO policy to support concerted efforts to organized immigrant labor regardless of legal status.[3] The AFL-CIO went from virulent antiimmigrant bashing to one of active support for organizing immigrants, after being pushed and prodded by labor and community activists to change its stance during the 1980s and 1990s as they realized that its future viability rested on the shoulders of immigrant workers (Hing, 2004, 182). However, the change in policy took several years; AFL-CIO President John Sweeney ran on a platform in 1995 to remove I-9 sanctions and provide resources to organize immigrant workers. In 1999, at the AFL-CIO National Convention, delegates voted to repeal I-9 sanctions (AFL-CIO Executive Council, 2000). At the following AFL-CIO Executive Council in February 2000, they voted to support a proimmigrant set of policies that reversed decades of antiimmigrant bashing (Ness, 2005, 42–3). They recognized the important role immigrants have historically played and would continue to play in the workplace and society and believed that immigrants should be entitled to full and fair workplace protections. As stated at the time, they believed the principles adopted in their statement on immigration should form national immigration policy including permanent legal status for undocumented, full workplace rights for immigrant workers (including the right to organize and protections for whistle-blowers), and punishment of business behavior that exploits workers for commercial gain (AFL-CIO, 2001).

By this time, several unions were already organizing and recruiting undocumented and immigrant workers into their ranks, including farm workers, food processing workers, meat packing workers, hotel and restaurant workers, garment workers, hospital workers, laundry workers, and many others. Virtually the entire service industry, meat packing, and light manufacturing rapidly turned over and became predominantly immigrant workers in the Southern California region and other parts of the country as massive Latino immigration and steady Asian American immigrants and refugees arrived seeking work, and unions sought to organize them. The contradictory practice of unions recruiting immigrant workers while labor's official policy was antiimmigrant was a major tipping point that led national labor leaders and labor activists to change AFL-CIO policy in favor of immigrants.

The second reason for Asian American participation in unionism is ethnic activism within the Asian American and Latino communities to mobilize its constituency. Much of the new immigrant labor movement has originated from California, starting in the 1980s with the Justice for Janitors campaign and organizing efforts in the garment and hotel industries. It is here that activists undertook the strenuous effort in "organizing the unorganizable," the vast immigrant labor pool (Bonacich and Gaspin, 2001; Engeman, 2014; Milkman, 2000). The efforts were not always successful, but it did build into a labor-based movement that embraced both work and immigrant issues. Latino militants led much of the effort; they melded community and labor organizing using street protests as much as strikes. Asians both benefited and participated in this social movement (Schneider, 2015; Wong, 2003, 2015). Organizations such as Asian Pacific American Labor Alliance (APALA), which was founded in 1992, played a key role in connecting Asian American workers and communities to the labor movement. Even before its founding convention, AAPI labor organizations in several cities had been working with AAPI workers and building their influence in select unions that were open to AAPI voices. After its founding, APALA has continued to hold annual organizing institutes to train rank-and-file members as organizers and leaders. APALA organizing institute graduates were then hired by unions as organizers. From 1992, Asian American organizers grew from a handful to a visible presence at every level of union structures in most of the major unions in the United States.

These efforts to include immigrant workers contributed to the sustained viability of unionism in California. The state's unionization rate is several percentage points higher than for the nation and has not experienced a secular decline (Adler, Tilly, and Thomas, 2015). The Asian American unionization rate in California is also higher than for the nation (14 percent vs. 12 percent). California has the highest density of the nation's AAPI workforce, with about three of ten residing in the state. Also, 40 percent of all AAPIs live in the Pacific region (Woo and Bucknor, 2015). The Northwest region has the best potential for increasing the percentage of AAPIs in unions in the coming decades.

Future Trajectory and Action Plan

The Asian American labor force will continue to grow over the foreseeable future. The U.S. Bureau of Labor Statistics projects that the number of Asian American workers will increase by more than 23 percent from 8.8 million in 2014 to 10.8 million by 2024, accounting for a quarter of the total net growth (U.S. Bureau of Labor Statistics, 2015). It is likely that this rapid growth rate will continue to 2040, with the Asian American labor force expanding faster than the Asian American population. In other words, Asian American workers will become an even more important component of the economy. Using a rough "back of the envelope" calculation based on the overall population projects and recent trends, Asian American workers will be about a tenth of the entire labor force by the middle of the century, if not earlier.[4]

Future Trends and Trajectory

By the year 2040, where will the jobs be? More so, by the year 2040, where will jobs for AAPIs be? If demographics are telling, there will be growth in caregiving, education, and technology.

Between 2015 and 2040, the number of elderly will increase 72 percent. By 2040, a staggering 22 percent of all Americans will elderly. There will be a heightened need for caregivers, many of who are already of AAPI descent. Today, approximately 1.8 million people are employed as domestic workers, most of whom work longer than eight-hour shifts, and make very little in terms of wages with few if any benefits (Burnham and Theodore, 2012; Dresser, 2008). While there are significant challenges to organizing workers who work in individual homes, the National Domestic Workers Alliance has focused on the unique challenges faced by this population of caregivers, who are 95 percent women, majority racial minority, and 45 percent immigrant (Burnham and Theodore, 2012). In many states across the nation, Service Employees International Union (SEIU) and the American Federation of State, County and Municipal Employees (AFSCME) have successfully organized home care workers, and these workers have seen their wages and working conditions rise. Community organizations have also organized thousands of domestic workers into domestic worker organizations and networks.

Other populations that will grow are children ages zero through five, K–12 children, and young adults. Given the shift toward lifelong learning, there will be increased demand for pre-K, K–12, higher education, and adult education. At the K–12 level, teacher demographics in public schools have not shifted to match the student population. Currently, more than 5 percent of all students in public K–12 are AAPI, but only 1.4 percent are AAPI teachers (Bristol, 2015). It is believed that AAPI teachers who are culturally and linguistically competent may be better able to address the needs of AAPI students, particularly among new immigrants and refugees. Currently, at the college level, there are more than 1.5 million faculty: 51 percent are full-time and 49 percent are part-time; 10 percent are AAPIs (U.S. Department of Education, National Center for Educational Statistics, 2015). However, 75 percent of all faculty are on temporary contracts and nontenure track (American Association of University Professors, 2016). Today's contingent faculty has depressed wages with one in four forced to survive on public assistance (Jacobs, Perry, MacGillvary, 2015). They have unstable working conditions from term to term and virtually no input in shared governance. This has prompted educated professionals, including AAPIs (adjunct, tenure track, and faculty at both public and private universities) to seek union representation from SEIU, the National Education Association, the American Federation of Teachers, the American Association of University Professors, and others. This type of sectoral unionization of highly educated professionals is possible by 2040.

The technology sector also employs highly educated professionals. Technology is expected to grow between now and 2040, and given the large proportion of Asian Americans with advanced educational degrees, it is likely that Asian American and Native Hawaiians and Pacific Islanders (NHPIs) will play important roles in an ever-increasing technology-driven economy. The question is whether or not Asian American workers in the tech industry will be employed in less than hospitable work environments and seek organization/union representation to get better working conditions. For example, if wages and benefits are depressed due to global competition, it could create more fertile ground for organizing tech professionals. Currently, more than 50 percent of California's Silicon Valley's workforce is Asian American and number in the tens of thousands (Nakaso, 2012). Many of the Asian American tech workers are immigrants who graduated from California state universities, and have been influenced by California's vibrant social movements. The tech field remains a key nonunion industry that could be impacted by a concerted unionization drive with an appropriate sectoral organizing strategy that addresses job protections and working conditions. There are several unions with the history and connections to tech-sector workers, particularly Asian American workers that could embark on a large-scale organizing drive in the coming period.

There are other sectors where Asian Americans work that are ripe for unionization. AAPIs are already heavily concentrated in the service industry where these opportunities exist and where union density is significant in certain states such as California and Nevada. AAPI women are also concentrated in hospitals and health care clinics; restaurants and other food services including hotels and casinos; and education including K–12 and postsecondary where future unionization efforts are likely to continue to grow (Woo and Buchnor, 2015). The bifurcation of the AAPI workforce that existed in 2015 is likely to continue into 2040 as new immigrants from Asia and the Pacific Islands are drawn to the United States, including professionals and entry-level low-wage workers many of whom will be reuniting with family members. Both segments will be needed in the 2040 economy.

Apprenticeship, Mentorship, and Leadership

The potential for organizing is strong, particularly as AAPI and non-AAPI union members apprentice and mentor other AAPIs to move into better paying union jobs, and move into union leadership. In fact, it is incumbent upon unions to develop a strategic plan to reach at least 10 percent of the 11+ million Asian American and NHPI workers by 2040. This is a realistic goal, given that in 2015, 9 percent or 788,000 of 8.8 million Asian American workers were union workers. With the right mentorship of young, middle-aged, and older workers, unions can organize across the life span, and improve the quality of life for all Americans by lifting up the pay, benefits, and working conditions of those they represent.

Within the labor movement, it is critical to build sustained efforts to mentor and develop more Asian American leaders in unions. At present, Asian American union leaders at the local, statewide, and national level are still small. Hawaii and California have the highest number of elected Asian American local/national union leaders in their respective unions. Josie Camacho is Executive Secretary-Treasurer of the Alameda County Central Labor Council in Northern California. She is the first Pacific Islander head of a local labor council on the mainland. Johanna Puno Hester, APALA National President, works with home care providers in the United Domestic Workers Union in San Diego, and is International Vice-President of the AFSCME union. Bhairavi Desai heads the National Taxi Workers Alliance and serves as the AFL-CIO National Executive Council. Luisa Blue and Maria Castaneda both sit on the SEIU International Executive Board and hold leadership positions at their locals. Maria Somma is the National Organizing Director for the United Steelworkers union. These and other AAPI union leaders are veterans of many organizing campaigns to unionize AAPI workers. They are to be tapped to mentor the next generation of AAPI labor leaders.

Indeed, another important role in the labor movement is to build internal mentorship programs to grow more AAPI leaders to mobilize the growing numbers of AAPIs and other racial minorities. The labor movement must continue to work with AAPI students to participate in organizing efforts, and recruit recent college graduates to join the labor movement as internal/external organizers and researchers. This generation of new AAPI entrants can have an influential role within unions to raise awareness of the importance of organizing AAPIs.

AAPIs also lead worker centers and national networks. The National Domestic Workers Alliance is led by Ai-jen Poo, the National Guestworkers Alliance by Saket Soni, the Restaurant Organizing Committee by Saru Jaramayan, and Jobs with Justice by Sarita Gupta. These organizations, along with the National Taxi Workers Alliance led by Bhairavi Desai, represent tens of thousands of workers, including significant numbers of AAPIs. The potential for AAPI growth in the broader labor movement including the worker center movement is very promising.

Conclusion: The Vision Forward

Asian Americans and NHPIs are two of the fastest-growing racial populations in America, and they are also among the fastest-growing racial segments of the U.S. labor market. We believe that AAPIs will continue to play a pivotal role in the U.S. economy and in the labor movement, both in the organized and the not-yet-organized segments.

The goal of this article is to explore the current and future potential for engaging AAPIs in the labor movement by increasing their density in union-organized occupations. Our goal is to engage at least 10 percent of the 11+ million AAPIs in the labor force by 2040. If we did so, we would be 1+ million AAPI unionized workers strong.

We believe that as AAPIs become a greater portion of the labor force, they will benefit from the increased attention by unions, and have the potential to become both the organized and the organizers. In so doing, AAPIs will have the opportunity to enhance the quality of life for all AAPIs, and all Americans, by the year 2040.

Notes

1. The American Federation of Labor under Samuel Gompers's leadership organized to drive Chinese workers out of the United States, resulting in the passage of the 1882 Chinese Exclusion Act, the first exclusionary immigration law. Unions also perceived the Chinese and other Asians as cheap and sometimes scab labor.

2. The labor force participation rate is defined as the proportion of the working-age population that is in the labor market (those participating), either employed or actively looking for work. The unemployment rate is the proportion of the labor force that is unemployed (without a job but actively looking for work). One indicator of economic status is occupation, which is correlated with earnings. The table includes one occupation toward the high end (management and business) and low end (sales and office) of the earnings ladder. For many, being employed full-year (at least fifty weeks) and full-time (at least thirty-five hours per week) (FT/FY) is desirable, so the table reports the proportion of the employed that are working FT/FY. Finally, we examine the median earnings of FT/FY workers, which eliminate the confounding effect of differences in level of employment.

3. The history of Asian Americans and unions is rather mixed. During the latter part of the nineteenth century, Chinese workers were attacked by white workers and organized labor (Kwong and Miscevic, 2005; Saxton, 1971; Tichenor, 2002). Asian Americans were excluded from joining unions in the early part of the twentieth century even as part of multiracial organizing efforts (Almaguer, 1994). Filipino agricultural workers during the 1920s and 1930s faced strong opposition from white workers, fueled by "long-standing racial animus towards Asiatics" (Ngai, 2004, p. 109). Things changed during the civil rights era. Filipinos were among the leaders who

organized farm workers and consumer boycotts against the grape industry, which lead to the establishment of the United Farm Workers.

4. This is based on the fact that the projected growth is disproportionately concentrated in the working-age segment, and it is likely that the labor force participation rate of women will increase.

References

Adler, Patrick, Tilly, Chris, and Trevor Thomas. 2015. "The State of the Unions in California and Its Key Cities in 2015." Los Angeles: UCLA Institute for Research on Labor and Employment.

AFL-CIO. 2001. "Immigration." 31 July. http://www.aflcio.org/About/Exec-Council/EC-Statements/Immigration (accessed March 3, 2016).

AFL-CIO Executive Council. 2000. "Immigration." Pp. 1–4 in *AFL-CIO Executive Council Actions*. AFL-CIO, Press Release, 16 February.

Allard, Mary Dorinda. 2011. "Asians in the U.S. Labor Force: Profile of a Diverse Population." *Monthly Labor Review* (November): 3-22.

Almaguer, Tomas. 1994. *Racial Fault Lines: The Historical Origins of White Supremacy in California*. Berkeley: University of California Press.

American Association of University Professors. 2016. "Background Facts on Contingent Faculty." http://www.aaup.org/issues/contingency/background-facts (accessed March 3, 2016).

Bonacich, Edna, and Fernando Gapasin. 2001. "Organizing the Unorganizable." Pp. 345-365 in *The State of California Labor*, ed. Paul Ong and James Lincoln. Los Angeles: University of California, Institute of Industrial Relations.

Bristol, Travis J. 2015. "Recruiting and Retaining Educators of Color." U.S. Department of Education. White House Initiative on Educational Excellence for African Americans. Stanford Center for Opportunity Policy in Education. Webinar, 7 May. http://sites.ed/gov/whieeaa/files/2014/Resource-Slides.pdf (accessed March 21, 2016).

Buckner, Cherrie. 2016. "Union Membership Byte 2016." Washington, DC: Center for Economic and Policy Research.

Burnham, Linda, and Nik Theodore. 2012. *Home Economics: The Invisible and Unregulated World of Domestic Work*. New York: National Domestic Workers Alliance.

Dresser, Laura. 2008. "Cleaning and Caring in the Home: Shared Problems? Shared Possibilities?" Pp. 111-136 in *The Gloves Off Economy: Workplace Standards at the Bottom of America's Labor Market*, ed. Annette Bernhardt, Heather Boushey, Laura Dresser, and Chris Tilly. Champaign: University of Illinois, Champaign-Urbana.

Engeman, Cassandra. 2014. "Social Movement Unionism in Practice: Organizational Dimensions of Union Mobilization in the Los Angeles Immigrant Rights Marches." *Work, Employment and Society*. http://wes.sagepub.com/content/early/2014/12/23/0950017014552027 (accessed March 15, 2016).

Hing, Bill Ong. 2004. *Defining American through Immigration Policy*. Philadelphia: Temple University Press.

Jacobs, Ken, Perry, Ian, and Jenifer MacGillvary. 2015. "The High Public Cost of Low Wages: Poverty-Level Wages Cost U.S. Taxpayers $152.8 Billion Each Year in Public Support for Working Families." UC Berkeley Center for Labor Research and Education, Research Brief, April. http://laborcenter.berkeley.edu/pdf/2015/the-high-public-cost-of-low-wages.pdf (accessed March 15, 2016).

Kim, Chang Hwan, and Yang Zhao. 2014. "Are Asian American Women Advantaged? Labor Market Performance of College Educated Female Workers." *Social Forces* 93(2): 623–52.

Kim, Marlene. 2011. "Asian American and Pacific Islanders: Employment Issues in the United States." *AAPI Nexus* 9 (1–2): 58–69.

Kim, Marlene, and Don Mar. 2007. "The Economic Status of Asian Americans." Pp. 148–84 in *Race and Economic Opportunity in the Twenty-First Century*, ed. Marlene Kim. Abingdon, UK: Routledge.

Kwong, Peter, and Dusanka Miscevic. 2005. *Chinese America: The Untold Story of America's Oldest New Community*. New York: The New Press.

Milkman, R. 2000. "Immigrant Organizing and the New Labor Movement in Los Angeles." *Critical Sociology* 26(1–2): 59–81.

Nakaso, Dan. 2012. "Tech Jobs: Citizen Asians Edge Non-citizen Asians. Some Fear Backlash as New Majority Forms in Bay Area." *Mercury News*, Bay Area News Group, 9 December.

Ness, Immanuel. 2005. *Immigrants, Unions, and the New U.S. Labor Market*. Philadelphia: Temple University Press.

Ngai, Mae M. 2004. *Impossible Subjects: Illegal Aliens and the Making of Modern America*. Princeton, NJ: Princeton University Press.

Rho, Hye Jin, John Schmitt, Nicole Woo, Lucia Lin and Kent Wong. 2011 "Diversity and Change: Asian American and Pacific Islander Workers." Center for Economic and Policy Research (CEPR). http://cepr.net/publications/reports/diversity-and-change. Accessed on April 21, 2016.

Saxton, Alexander. 1971. *The Indispensable Enemy: Labor and the Anti-Chinese Movement in California*. Berkeley: University of California Press.

Schmitt, John, and Kris Warner. 2010. "The Changing Face of US Labor, 1983–2008." *WorkingUSA* 13(2): 263–79.

Schmitt, John, Rho, Hye Jin, and Nicole Woo. 2011. "Unions and Upward Mobility for Asian American and Pacific Islander Workers." Center for Economic and Policy Research. http://cepr.net/publications/reports/unions-and-upward-mobility-for-asian-american-and-pacific-islander-workers (accessed March 15, 2016).

Schneider, Daniel. 2015. "Organized Labor and the Unionization of Hispanic, Chinese, and Filipino Americans." *Labor Studies Journal* 40(2): 169–95.

Shiu, Patricia. 2014. "Closing the Pay Gap for Asian American Women." U.S Department of Labor Blog, 3 June. https://blog.dol.gov/2014/06/03/closing-the-pay-gap-for-asian-american-women/ (accessed March 15, 2016).

Tichenor, Daniel J. 2002. *The Dividing Line: The Politics of Immigration Control in America*. Princeton, NJ: Princeton University Press.

U.S. Bureau of Labor Statistics. 2015. "Employment Projections. Civilian Labor Force by Detailed Age, Gender, Race, and Ethnicity." http://www.bls.gov/emp/ep_table_304.htm. (accessed on March 15, 2016).

U.S. Department of Education, National Center for Education Statistics. 2015. "Characteristics of Postsecondary Faculty." The Condition of Education 2015 (NCES 2015-144). https://nces.ed.gov/programs/coe/indicator_cuf.asp (accessed March 15, 2016).

Wong, Kent. 2015. "A New Labor Movement for a New Working Class: Unions, Worker Centers, and Immigrants." *Berkeley Journal of Employment and Labor Law* 36(1): 205–13.

———. 2003. "Building an Asian Pacific Labor Alliance: A New Chapter in Our History." *Asian American Politics: Law, Participation, and Policy* 3: 421–30.

Woo, Nicole, and Cherrie Bucknor. 2015. "Asian American and Pacific Islander Workers Today." Center for Economic and Policy Research, Issue Brief, May.

———

Johanna Hester's dedication to working families began in the 1990s when she successfully organized two thousand recreation and park assistants in Los Angeles as Lead Organizer for AFSCME. Since her early organizing days, Johanna has become a formidable labor leader, champion for home care providers, and outspoken advocate for the immigrant and civil rights of workers. She currently represents the United Domestic Workers, is an International Vice President of AFSCME, and is National President of APALA. Johanna also recently completed the Senior Executives in State and Local Government program with the Harvard Kennedy School.

Kim Geron is Professor of Political Science at California State University East Bay. He is currently 2nd Vice President of APALA and Alameda Chapter President. He is also the Vice President of the California Faculty Association. His research focuses on labor and racial politics.

Tracy Lai is a tenured historian at Seattle Central College where she teaches U.S. history, and Asian, Asian American, and women studies. She serves as National Secretary for APALA, Co-chair of Seattle APALA, and Vice President for Human Rights, American Federation of Teachers, Washington.

Paul M. Ong is a professor at UCLA's Luskin School of Public Affairs and UCLA's Asian American Studies Department. He is currently the Director of the UCLA Center for Neighborhood Knowledge, founding editor of *AAPI Nexus: Policy, Practice and Community*, and founding director of the UC AAPI Policy Multi-Campus Research Program. He has conducted research on immigration, civic and political participation, economic status of minorities, welfare-to-work, health workers, urban spatial inequality, and environmental inequality.

Practitioners Essay

Aging in America:
Asian Americans and Pacific Islanders in 2040

Heather Chun, Eun Jeong Lee, Wesley Lum,
and Ashley Muraoka-Mamaclay

Abstract

Throughout the United States ten thousand people turn sixty-five years old every day (AARP, 2015a). By 2040, one in five U.S. residents will be sixty-five years or older, outnumbering children fifteen and younger for the first time in our nation's history (AARP, 2015a; Congressional Budget Office, 2013; U.S. Census Bureau, 2014). Between 2015 and 2040, Asian American and Pacific Islander (AAPI) older adults are the fastest-growing aging group. There are four strategies to strengthen the economic and health security of AAPI older adults nationwide by 2040: (1) disaggregate data to understand variations between AAPI subpopulations; (2) provide accessible services that are culturally and linguistically appropriate; (3) adapt mainstream solutions for financial security; and (4) innovate long-term services and support.

Introduction

In 1952, when Ling was three, she left Guangzhou, China, and settled in Hawaii with her mother, Mei, and four siblings. Ling's younger siblings left Hawaii to pursue careers when their mother was still working full-time making manapua at the same restaurant she had been employed at since their migration. In 2010, Ling received a call from Mei's boss concerned about her mother's ability to perform tasks. At the age of eighty-two, Mei was diagnosed with dementia. Over the past five years, Ling has been living with and caring for her mother, whose health has been deteriorating due to dementia's rapid progression. Since her retirement, Mei's income has been limited to Social Security, with no retirement savings, relying on Medicare and Medicaid to cover her rapidly rising health care expenditures. Mei's Social Security payments only cover a third of her monthly rent. Despite hopes of financial security, Ling's siblings are living on fixed incomes and unable to assist with the rising cost of Mei's care.

I cannot shake the sadness I feel for Ling and Mei, whose situation has become increasingly commonplace. I wreck my brain trying to answer, "How are we going to meet the growing and diverse needs of older adults? As the number of those aging in society grows in 2040, is the answer to invest more public funding into services to care for the aged, or do we transform aging services to serve future consumers differently?"

Aging in America: Asian Americans and Pacific Islanders

Throughout the United States ten thousand people turn sixty-five years old every day, a trend that will continue for the next fifteen years (AARP, 2015a). By 2040, one in five U.S. residents will be sixty-five years or older, outnumbering children fifteen and younger for the first time in our nation's history (AARP, 2015a; Congressional Budget Office, 2013). The definition of an older adult lacks uniformity, with an arbitrary range between fifty and sixty-five years of age. Most commonly, however, the chronological age assigned to measure the aging population is based upon pensionable age limits. In developed nations, people are most often able to begin collecting pension benefits at the age of sixty-five and, as such, this is often the marker assigned to data collection on older adults.

As the longevity of our nation increases, a rapid demographic shift is visible across diverse ethnic groups as well. Asian American and Pacific Islander (AAPI) older adults aged sixty-five years and older is the fastest-growing aging group. In 2015, more than two million AAPI older adults reside in the United States, representing 4.64 percent of the national aging population and 10 percent of the total AAPI population (Ong, 2016). In 2010, across AAPI ethnic groups, the fastest-growing populations of older adults were Chinese (accounting for 26 percent of AAPI elders), Filipinos, Japanese, Indians, and Koreans (ibid.). Between now and 2040, alike with other ethnicities, the rise in older adults will find those sixty-five years and older representing a larger percentage of their respective populations. During the next quarter century, Pacific Islander older adults will increase from 7 percent to 13 percent of the Pacific Islander population, and Asian American older adults from 10 percent to 16 percent of the Asian American population (Ong, Ong, and Ong, 2016a; Ong, Ong, and Ong, 2016b).

Among the many reasons for an increasing AAPI population, the rapid growth rate is largely due to immigration, contrary to the argument that immigration is slowing the aging of our society. Immigration will continue to have an impact on the impeding demographic shift and increase the percentage of retirees into the future (Camarota, 2012). In 2010, 80 percent of AAPI elders were foreign-born, and 65 percent had become naturalized citizens of the United States (National Asian Pacific Center on Aging, 2013b). The majority of those who are foreign-born have lived in the United States for twenty-one years or more. At a disaggregated glance, the dissimilarity on immigration between ethnic subgroups is vast, however. More than 97 percent of Bangladeshis, Cambodians, Vietnamese, Indonesians, Asian Indians, and Sri Lankans sixty-five years and older are foreign-born, compared with 32 percent of Samoans (ibid.). The continuously changing ethnic profile and immigration history of older Americans requires policy makers to pay particular attention to the unique needs of AAPI older adults.

A rapidly aging population demands public attention to develop proactive approaches. This includes paying particular attention to policies impacting social determinants of health, such as the economic and health security of a diverse and growing population of older adults. Combined, the economic and health status of our nation's older adults will have profound impacts on federal and state support systems, for example Social Security, Medicare, and long-term services and supports (LTSS) through the Older American's Act, such as with Mei's example. Older adults' reliance on Social Security and Medicare challenges many to maintain self-sufficiency as they become more frail and in need of care.

In 2015, during the White House Conference on Aging, aging organizations, older adult advocates, and public entities agreed with several public policy priorities to address the imminent demographic shift. By 2040, policy issues—such as rebuilding the foundations of retirement security; transforming our health care system; developing a comprehensive approach that provides access to quality LTSS, including support for caregivers; strengthening quality and safety protections for vulnerable older adults; and enabling older adults to remain active and connected to their communities—will have commanded solutions. As we look toward 2040, without reform, policy issues that impact older adults will also extend to AAPI elders, such as solutions to economic security as people age and the complexity of illnesses such as Alzheimer's Disease and related dementias. Additional challenges, however, elevate the difficulty of fostering AAPI elders' economic and health security.

Limited English Proficiency

Limited English proficiency (LEP) can isolate AAPI older adults, the majority of whom are foreign-born. In 2010, only 15 percent of AAPI older adults spoke English at home; 60 percent had LEP (National Asian Pacific Center on Aging, 2013b). Thirty-one percent of AAPI older adults are linguistically isolated, meaning that all members of the household speak English less than "very well" (ibid.). There are substantial sub-population variations, however. More than 85 percent of Cambodian, Vietnamese, Hmong, and Laotian older adults are LEP, whereas the lowest rates among AAPIs are with Native Hawaiians, with only 2 percent of elders being linguistically isolated (ibid.).

The LEP of many AAPI elders often restricts their access to vital information, supports, and services. Systems that support older adults, such as health care and legal systems, must become integrated, culturally competent, and linguistically accessible. Eliminating the silos that currently exist between the systems of support will allow for the needs of AAPI older adults to be prioritized. For example, with stronger linkages between systems, a hospital social worker could identify an LEP older adult in need of an advanced health care directive and/or estate planning. The social worker would be aware of culturally appropriate services and communicate directly with the in-language legal service provider to facilitate assistance for the older adult. Once integrated, AAPI older adults will have access to in-language, culturally competent service systems that are person centered and consumer directed; simply put, these services will be led by the AAPI older adult and tailored to their individual strengths, goals, preferences, needs, and desired outcomes.

Economic Security

A commonly believed myth of AAPIs is that they are all self-sufficient and upwardly mobile. However, the prevalence of poverty is severe when disaggregating the data by ethnic groups. In 2010, more than one in five Koreans (20.4 percent), Tongans (21.2 percent), Hmong (21.5 percent), and Marshallese (29.9 percent) elders sixty-five years and older were below the poverty level, yet older adult Malaysian households had a median income of $90,625, well exceeding the U.S. median income of $33,906 (National Asian Pacific Center on Aging, 2013c). Among the most impoverished AAPI older adult subpopulations are Hmong older adults, who have a median household income of $18,598, and Bhutanese, of whom 63 percent are living in poverty (ibid.).

Far exceeding other ethnic groups, AAPI elders often live in overcrowded households, or those with more than one person per room. Sixty-two percent of Bhutanese live in overcrowded homes compared with 14.6 percent of Bangladeshi (ibid.). Home ownership and housing costs vary drastically. Three percent of Bhutanese older adults are home owners compared to 83 percent of Taiwanese, and approximately 40 percent of AAPI older adults are spending more than 30 percent of their income on housing (ibid.).

Without intervention, there will be an increase in AAPI older adults reliant on Social Security and other publicly funded benefits to remain economically stable. Social Security benefits are an important source of income for AAPI older adults, with 26 percent of older adult married couples and 52 percent of those unmarried relying on their benefits for 90 percent or more of their income (ibid.). For refugees and recent immigrants, however, the ability to retain this benefit hinges upon citizenship. AAPIs entering the United States may receive Social Security for up to seven years, at which point they must obtain citizenship or risk losing their benefits (ibid.). Average Social Security incomes range from $2,659 to $10,867 per year for AAPI subpopulations (National Asian Pacific Center on Aging, 2013c). AAPI older adults also disproportionately rely on food stamps, with 14 percent collecting this benefit compared to 9 percent of the U.S. population sixty-five years and older (AARP, 2014b).

Paving the way to 2040 will require economic options for AAPI older adults that extend beyond Social Security, for example, other forms of savings and pensions. The voices of AAPI elders are amplifying the significance of additional options to support their retirement security and self-sufficiency. An analysis of AAPI older adults employed in New York City revealed that a staggering 63 percent were not confident they will be able to retire (ibid.). AAPI older adults' high dependence on Social Security benefits is also leading to longer and higher labor force participation, compared to U.S. total population (42.5 percent vs. 38.1 percent, respectively, among aged fifty-five years and older) (National Asian Pacific Center on Aging, 2013c). Only 22 percent of AAPI elders have retirement income, compared to 37 percent of the older adult population throughout the United States (AARP, 2014b). Although financial challenges afflict all ethnicities, there are additional challenges to AAPI older adults' economic security that must be considered.

Health Insurance

The lack of health insurance coverage has profound impacts on AAPI older adults' economic and health security. AAPI older adults are more likely to be covered by Medicare only, or Medicare and Medicaid, compared to the U.S. population (National Asian Pacific Center on Aging, 2013c). Only 33 percent of Asians have private insurance, compared to 52 percent of older adults nationally (ibid.). Of grave concern, the uninsured rate of AAPI older adults far exceeds the national rate. Seven out of the top ten uninsured ethnic groups in the United States are AAPIs (National Council of Asian Pacific Islander Physicians, 2015). For example, 23 percent of Bangladeshi, 15 percent Tongan, and 15 percent of Pakistani older adults were uninsured, compared to 1 percent of the total U.S. older adult population (National Asian Pacific Center on Aging, 2013c).

Enactment of the Patient Protection and Affordable Care Act (ACA) highlights a promising future for accessible health care among all Americans, including AAPI older adults. The launch of the ACA found 1.4 million AAPI older adults eligible for health insurance (National Asian Pacific Center on Aging, 2012). Although ACA enrollment data on AAPIs is limited and difficult to find, it was estimated that only six hundred thousand AAPIs gained insurance after the first round of ACA enrollment. This leaves 1.2 million remaining uninsured (Ramakrishnan and Ahmad, 2014).

By 2040, it is critical to mitigate barriers that impact AAPI older adults from receiving equitable access to health care. For example, the lack of culturally and linguistically competent resources, poor health literacy, unreliable enrollment platforms, immigration-related verification issues, funding challenges, and insufficient state policies have been cited as a few of the challenges afflicting AAPI older adults (National Council of Asian Pacific Islander Physicians, 2015). A serious lack of in-language resources to assist and educate AAPI older adults in ACA enrollment is of particular concern. A recent analysis revealed that the majority of in-language ACA resources on federal and state websites were in English and Spanish (ibid.). Although AAPIs have been targeted in outreach efforts for ACA enrollment, in-language resources are not readily available and those that exist often require extensive navigation through websites, many of which are in English and pose an additional barrier (ibid.). Access to in-language resources that guide ACA enrollment is critical because of the increase of LEP AAPI elders who remain uninsured.

Health Disparities

The health and functional challenges faced by AAPI older adults are similar to the issues afflicting the aggregated older adult population throughout the United States. However, the prevalence and impacts they have on AAPI subpopulations vary extensively. Looking at AAPI older adults' disability status—that is, collectively considering their functional limitations, limitations in activities of daily living, cognitive problems, and blindness or deafness—the highest disability rates are evident among Native Hawaiians, Pacific Islanders, and Vietnamese older adults, although the specific disability issues are very different (Fuller-Thompson, Brennenstuhl, and Hurd, 2011). Vietnamese older adults, for example, have a disproportionately high prevalence of cognitive problems (16.6 percent), more than double the rate for Koreans at 7.6 percent (ibid.). Likewise, Native Hawaiian older adults have higher rates of obesity and type 2 diabetes (ibid.). Additionally, Native Hawaiian women have the highest overall cancer death rates out of any ethnicity (ibid.).

Disability outcomes for AAPI older adults are largely affected by education and immigration variables, such as immigration history, citizenship status, and whether or not English is spoken at home (ibid.). When the data is adjusted to accommodate these variables, Native Hawaiians and Pacific Islanders have a higher risk of cognitive issues and activities of daily living impairments, which is two times the risk as compared to Chinese older adults (ibid.).

Of particular concern when considering the health disparities faced by AAPI older adults is their underrepresentation in long-term care facilities. Institutionalization rates vary among AAPI older adults with functional limitations, from 4.7 percent of Asian Indians to 18.8 percent of Korean Americans (Fuller-Thompson and Chi, 2012). Compared to other AAPI subpopulations, Vietnamese older adults have the highest rates of cognitive problems yet the lowest rates of institutionalization (ibid.). Of those most likely to be placed in a nursing home are AAPI older adults eighty-five years and older and those with cognitive problems (ibid.). Notably, AAPI older adults are twice as likely to be placed in an institution if they speak English at home (ibid.). Health care professionals and policy makers should pay particular attention to the barriers to long-term care settings facing AAPI older adults such as citizenship status, prohibitive costs, English proficiency, food preferences, acculturation, and cultural norms (ibid.). Bridging the language gap between AAPI older adults and health care providers is also vital. For example, a provider's ability to understand how language is used to express concerns and what assumptions are brought by AAPI older adults to health care exchanges are essential to ensuring equitable health care for AAPI older adults by 2040.

Without sufficient resources (such as health insurance), health disparities among AAPI older adults will remain prevalent. Similar to other areas of research on AAPI older adults, and as illustrated through the examples provided within this section, disaggregated data is needed to understand the health disparities faced by the subpopulations. By 2040, disaggregated data will equip health care professionals and policy makers to tailor services, reduce or eliminate health disparities, and provide better access to health care. The role of community-based organizations will continue to be important, as these organizations are often the strongest linkage between AAPI older adults and their community.

Caregiving

Traditional values, such as filial piety, play a role in AAPI older adults' access to health care, institutionalization, and the entire family's economic security. AAPI older adults and their families may perceive institutionalization and formal health care as stigmatizing (ibid.). As many AAPI older adults are foreign-born they are less acculturated than their children, which may isolate the older adult from health care systems and from their communities.

With less reliance on formal systems, AAPI families commonly rely on the family unit to care for one another, and the children are often expected to care for their aging parents. Seventy-three percent of AAPIs believe that caring for parents is expected of them (AARP, 2014a). A disaggregated prevalence of caregiving among AAPI families has not yet been documented; however, according to an AARP survey, 42 percent of AAPI respondents were providing care to an older adult compared to 22 percent of the general population (ibid.). Collectively, more than half of the care provided to older adults throughout the United States is provided by family members and friends (Congressional Budget Office, 2013). During times of increasing strains on the economic health of the United States, caregiving demands a significant dedication, often finding people challenged to adequately uphold their other responsibilities, such as paid employment. With so many AAPI older adults being cared for by family members, it is imperative that caregiving family members receive adequate support to maintain their economic security and ability to care for their families into the future. Caregivers are critical to the viability of the U.S. health care system, with a value of care that was totaled to be approximately $234 billion in 2011 (Congressional Budget Office, 2013).

Recommendations and Strategies for the Future

In conclusion, we present four policy recommendations. Once/if accomplished by 2040 these recommendations will have significantly strengthened the economic and health security of AAPI older adults nationwide. To be successful, the civic engagement of AAPI older adults must be leveraged. Maximizing the political power of AAPI older adults, while making forward progress on the recommendations presented, requires close partnerships with community-based organizations; these organizations have strong connections to the diverse communities they serve, with solid track records for activating AAPI civic engagement. If effectively mobilized, the political power of AAPI older adults in 2040 will become paramount, as those sixty-five years and older will account for a substantial percentage of the American voter base. Policy issues that have a direct impact on their well-being, as well as problems that AAPI older adults find to be especially important, will command policy solutions.

1. Disaggregated Data

The ethnic distinctions between AAPI elders calls for a reevaluation of the priorities of public policy and national perceptions of this burgeoning demographic. Robust variations between AAPI subpopulations must be understood and acknowledged to appropriately determine public policy solutions. Aggregating AAPI older adults into one ethnic category obscures meaningful differences between subpopulations. Analyzing the needs of AAPI older adults collectively masks unique subpopulation issues, leading to "one-size-fits-all" public policies that do not comprehensively meet the needs of all older adults. As such, it is recommended that a national policy for data collection for AAPIs be designed, with cross tabs to standardized age categories. Additionally, the national policy and standards should be integrated into federal survey tools (e.g., the U.S. Census).

2. Culturally and Linguistically Appropriate Services

The availability of linguistically accessible information will be essential for AAPI older adults to achieve economic and health security by 2040. Systemically, a more robust integration of AAPI language bilingual staff to conduct front-line work with older adults is crucial. Additional funding for in-language resources (e.g., additional bilingual staff; interpreter services; and in-language programs, services, resources, and websites) is recommended. Finally, as federal and local policies (e.g., the Office of Minority Health's Culturally and Linguistically Appropriate Services in Health Care standards—the Enhanced National CLAS Standard and the ACA) recognize the vast number of older Americans who have LEP, ongoing education and monitoring with local providers will be necessary to facilitate stronger health equity among AAPI older adults.

3. Mainstream Solutions for Financial Security

Mentioned earlier, many AAPI older adults rely on their Social Security benefits for 90 percent or more of their income (National Asian Pacific Center on Aging, 2013c). The increasing reliance on Social Security is not unique to AAPI older adults, however. The "three-legged stool for retirement," a historical metaphor used to describe the necessary components for financial security into retirement (Social Security, pension, and personal savings), is outdated. Developing financial security among older Americans is challenging; however, as federal expenditures for Social Security, Medicare, and Medicaid increase with our rapidly aging demographic, there is an urgent need for efficient solutions.

For AAPI older adults to maintain financial security by 2040, it's recommended that mainstream solutions consider the unique needs of this diverse population. In addition, as evidenced by the National Asian Pacific Center on Aging's pilot study of Senior Community Service Employment Program participants, many AAPI older adults have low levels of financial literacy (National Asian Pacific Center on Aging, 2014). In-language financial education, information, and services are needed to strengthen financial literacy among AAPI older adults, thereby fostering their financial security.

4. LTSS Innovation

Similarly, the federal budget cannot sustain the increasing costs of care for the expanding population of older Americans. LTSS, or the care provided to help people meet their functional needs (such as assistance with bathing or managing medications), are most commonly provided in the community. The demand for LTSS will rise dramatically as we approach 2040 (Congressional Budget Office, 2013). While more cost-effective and preferred than institutional care, LTSS are expensive, accounting for $192 billion in 2011, with the largest payers being Medicare and Medicaid (ibid.). Not factored into this economic value is the growing importance of informal caregivers, who provided approximately $234 billion in care in 2011 (ibid.).

Elevating the care required for normative aging, challenging diseases (such as Alzheimer's Disease and related dementias) and complex issue areas (such as financial exploitation) demand solutions that will enable people to remain safe and age with a high quality of life. Again, as mainstream solutions are developed for systems that will care for older Americans into the future, the unique needs of AAPI older adults must be considered. With the increasing complexity of care, it's also recommended that incentives for innovations in LTSS be provided. By invigorating systems that deliver care to a more diverse cohort of older Americans, there is an opportunity for major government health care programs to be solvent, while also enabling both the economic and health security of older adults and their families. Lastly, as improvements to care systems are made, supports for informal caregivers must become more robust, and as with the cultural considerations recommended for systems that support older adults, systems that support informal caregivers must also consider the unique needs of AAPIs.

Reflecting on the Future

It is the summer of 2040. Ling and I are slowly walking around her Chinatown neighborhood, reminiscing about the changes that have occurred over the past two decades. Twenty years ago, I cared for Ling's mother, Mei, and now I am assisting Ling with managing her LTSS. Despite her age of eighty-nine and minor chronic conditions, Ling has been able to manage her health, reside independently, and access sufficient LTSS. Ling's adult children have moved to other states, but her granddaughter lives with her and helps Ling manage her care. Some of Ling's friends opted to reside in long-term care facilities, as they've made drastic improvements, now providing culturally and linguistically appropriate services. The facilities employ many bilingual and bicultural staff, and the residents enjoy living there. Ling had the option to move in, but she decided that self-directing her own care and living at home with her granddaughter was what she preferred. Since the reform of Social Security and Medicare, Ling's publicly funded benefits have paid for most of her basic living and health care costs, although on some occasions, she dips into her retirement savings. Ling often talks to me about her mother, Mei, who lived with dementia long ago. Ling and I reflect on the improvements to the systems that enable her to remain active and living in her community, the same community where she cared for her mother just twenty years earlier.

References

AARP. 2015a. "The Priorities Book: Building a Better Future 2015–2016." http://www.aarp.org/content/dam/aarp/about_aarp/aarp_policies/2015-05/

AARP-Priorities-Book-2015-2016.pdf (accessed March 7, 2016).

———. 2014a. "Caregiving among Asian Americans and Pacific Islanders Age 50+." http://www.aarp.org/content/dam/aarp/home-and-family/caregiving/2014-11/caregiving_aapis_english.pdf (accessed March 7, 2016).

———. 2014b. "Are Asian Americans and Pacific Islanders Financially Secure?" http://www.aarp.org/content/dam/aarp/home-and-family/caregiving/2014-11/AARP-Report-Are-Asian-Americans-and-Pacific-Islanders-Financially-Secure-Dec2014-eng.pdf (accessed March 7, 16).

Camarota, Steven. 2012. "Projecting Immigration's Impact on the Size and Age Structure of the 21st Century American Population." Center for Immigration Studies. http://cis.org/projecting-immigrations-impact-on-the-size-and-age-structure-of-the-21st-century-american-population (accessed March 7, 2016).

Congressional Budget Office. 2013. "Rising Demand for Long-Term Services and Supports for Elderly People." https://www.cbo.gov/sites/default/files/113th-congress-2013-2014/reports/44363-LTC.pdf (accessed March 7, 2016).

Fuller-Thompson, Esme, and Monica Chi. 2012. "Older Asian Americans and Pacific Islanders with Activities of Daily Living (ADL) Limitations: Immigration and Other Factors Associated with Institutionalization." *International Journal of Environmental Research and Public Health* 9: 3264–79.

Fuller-Thompson, Esme, Brennenstuhl, Sarah, and Marion Hurd. 2011. "Comparison of Disability Rates among Older Adults in Aggregated and Separate Asian American/Pacific Islander Subpopulations." *American Journal of Public Health* 101(1): 94–100.

National Asian Pacific Center on Aging. 2014. "Financial Well-Being among Low-Income Asian Older Workers: Evidence from Senior Community Service Employment Program Participants." http://napca.org/wp-content/uploads/2014/06/SCSEP-financial-well-being-FINAL.pdf (accessed March 7, 2016).

———. 2013b. "Asian American and Pacific Islanders in the United States Aged 65 Years and Older: Population, Nativity, and Language. Data Brief, 1, 3." http://napca.org/wp-content/uploads/2013/10/65+-population-report-FINAL.pdf (accessed March 7, 2016).

———. 2013c. "Asian Americans and Pacific Islanders in the United States Aged 65 Years and Older: Economic Indicators. Data Brief, 1, 4." http://napca.org/wp-content/uploads/2013/10/economic-indicators-FINAL.pdf (accessed March 7, 2016).

———. 2012. "Press Release: NAPCA Statement on the Affordable Care Act Ruling." http://napca.org/wp-content/uploads/2013/01/062812AffordableCareAct.pdf.pdf (accessed January 13, 2016).

National Council of Asian Pacific Islander Physicians. 2015. "The Impact of the Affordable Care Act on Asian Indian, Chinese, Filipino, Korean, Pakistani, and Vietnamese Americans." https://d3n8a8pro7vhmx.cloudfront.net/ncapa/pages/110/attachments/original/1437158772/2015_ACA_policy_brief_ v13_final.pdf?1437158772 (accessed March 7, 2016).

Ong, Jonathan, Ong, Paul, and Elena Ong. 2016a. "The Future of Asian America in 2040." *AAPI Nexus Journal: Policy, Practice, and Community* 14(1): 14–29.

———. 2016b. "The Future of Pacific Islander America in 2040." *AAPI Nexus Journal: Policy, Practice, and Community* 14(1): 1–13.

Ramakrishnan, Karthick, and Farah Ahmad. 2014. "Immigration: Part of the 'State of Asian Americans and Pacific Islanders' Series." Center for American Progress. https://www.americanprogress.org/issues/race/report/2014/04/23/87520/state-of-asian-americans-and-pacific-islanders-series/ (accessed March 7, 2016).

HEATHER CHUN, MSW, is the Director of Technical Assistance at the National Asian Pacific Center on Aging. Heather has studied and worked in the human service field for more than ten years. Her experience in aging policy, program development and evaluation, and advocacy have focused on areas related to caregiving, elder abuse, Alzheimer's Disease and related dementias, long-term services and supports, community planning, and volunteerism.

DR. EUN JEONG LEE has been a champion for more than twenty-five years in Korea and the United States helping elders, women, children, the disabled, and victims of domestic violence. Currently, Dr. Lee is currently the National Director of the National Asian Pacific Center on Aging Senior Community Service Employment Program. Additionally, Dr. Lee has also conducted several research studies about financial well-being, elder mistreatment, and heart health among AAPI elders. Dr. Lee holds a BA in journalism and mass communication and MPA in public administration from Hanyang University in Korea, and a PhD in social welfare from Yeshiva University in New York.

WES LUM is the President and CEO of the National Asian Pacific Center on Aging (NAPCA). Prior to his appointment to NAPCA, Dr. Lum was the Director of the Executive Office on Aging. Dr. Lum has also held positions as an Assistant Professor at the University of Hawaii School of Social Work, Specialist at the University of Hawaii Center on Aging, Director of Government Affairs at the Chamber of Commerce of Hawaii, and as a legislative analyst in the state House of Representatives Majority Staff Office. Dr. Lum has a PhD and MA in sociology, and a MPH from University of Hawaii–Manoa.

ASHLEY MURAOKA-MAMACLAY, MURP, is the Director of Outreach and Education at the National Asian Pacific Center on Aging, and has worked in the field of aging for more than ten years. She has done extensive research in the areas of naturally occurring retirement communities, universal design, aging in place, elder-friendly communities, land use, and community-based planning. Her experience in aging includes long-term services and supports delivery systems, Senior Corps: RSVP, evidence-based healthy aging programs, aging and disability resource centers, benefits enrollment centers, long-term care, and No Wrong Door.

aapi nexus Vol. 14, No. 1 (Spring 2016): 110-129

Practitioners Essay

Forging a Path
Toward Health Equity in 2040

Priscilla Huang, Kathy Ko Chin, Jeffrey B. Caballero,
DJ Ida, and Myron Dean Quon

Abstract

Dramatic shifts in the demographic makeup of the U.S. population in 2040 will pose new challenges and opportunities for policy makers, researchers, and community members working to address health and health care inequities. Traditional approaches utilizing a health disparities framework may not be enough to address the health needs of an increasingly diverse and multiracial population of Asian Americans and Native Hawaiians and Pacific Islanders (NHPIs). This article provides an overview of the current and projected health and health care needs of Asian Americans and NHPIs in 2040, and proposes new policy solutions and frameworks for addressing these complex needs.

Introduction

In a little more than a generation, almost half of the United States population will be a person of color (U.S. Census Bureau, 2015a). Asian Americans and Native Hawaiians and Pacific Islanders (NHPIs) will account for the fastest population growth, constituting nearly one in ten Americans (Ong , Ong, and Ong, 2016).[1]

Diversity in the United States will also become increasingly complex, as more and more Americans identify as multiracial. Multiracial Asian Americans in particular are projected to lead the pack with a 130 percent growth (ibid.). There will also be notable differences by generation; Asian Americans and Pacific Islanders twenty-nine years and younger will more likely be U.S.-born, while Asian Americans and Pacific Islanders sixty years and older will more likely be foreign-born (ibid.).

These dramatic shifts in the demographic makeup of the future U.S. population will pose new challenges and opportunities for policy makers, researchers, and community members as they continue to tackle health and health care inequities.[2] Traditionally, advocates utilized a health disparities framework to analyze differences in health outcomes, conditions, and health care service delivery based on race. Under this framework, researchers made comparisons between minority populations and the majority white population. They also developed policy solutions and interventions that targeted specific racial and ethnic populations. Yet, as the country shifts toward a "minority majority" population, will a disparities approach be the most appropriate way to address health needs, particularly for Asian Americans and NHPIs?

Current State of Health and Health Care for Asian Americans and NHPIs

An estimated 20.3 million Asian Americans and 1.5 million NHPIs currently reside in the United States (U.S. Census Bureau, 2015b). Asian Americans and NHPIs are comprised of diverse groups originating from more than fifty different countries and speaking more than one hundred languages and dialects (Pew Research Center, 2012). One in five Asian Americans is "limited English proficient (LEP)," meaning the individual speaks English less than very well (Zong and Batalova, 2015). About 60 percent of Asian Americans are foreign-born, representing the highest proportion of foreign-born among all racial groups in the United States. Among Pacific Islanders, more than one in seven are foreign-born (Empowering Pacific Islander Communities and Asian Americans Advancing Justice, 2014).

Uninsured rates among Asian Americans and NHPIs are comparable to the general U.S. population—in 2013, about 15 percent of Asian Americans and 18 percent of NHPIs lacked health insurance compared with 15 percent of the overall U.S. population (U.S. Census Bureau, 2013). However, uninsured rates vary dramatically when disaggregated by ethnic group. For example, Pakistanis, Koreans, and Bangladeshi all have rates of 22 percent or higher (Asian & Pacific Islander American Health Forum, 2012a). Asian American and NHPI children also experience high rates of being uninsured or underinsured.[3] Approximately 8 percent of Asian American children and 11 percent of NHPI children are uninsured. Asian American children also have the highest rate of underinsurance among all racial groups, at 20 percent (Asian & Pacific Islander American Health Forum, 2011a). These disparities in coverage rates correlate with income differences among Asian Americans and NHPIs. Despite popular perceptions of Asian Americans and NHPIs as high achieving and financially prosperous, nearly two million are poor (National Coalition for Asian Pacific American Community Development, 2013).[4] The 2007 recession also demonstrated that many more live on the brink of poverty. Asian Americans, NHPIs, and Latinos were the hardest hit by the recession, which increased the number of poor Asian Americans and NHPIs by 38 percent (ibid.).

Asian Americans and NHPIs also experience certain diseases and chronic conditions at a higher rate than other racial groups. The rate of Asian Americans suffering from tuberculosis was more than twenty times higher than that of non-Hispanic whites from 1993 to 2012 (Centers for Disease Control, 2013). Approximately one out of two individuals with chronic hepatitis B is Asian American or Pacific Islander (Centers for Disease Control, 2015a). Diabetes and overweight/obesity prevalence also poses a serious threat to Asian American and NHPI health. NHPIs have a higher prevalence of diagnosed diabetes at over 14 percent compared to non-Hispanic whites at 8 percent. (Centers for Disease Control, 2015b). Asian Americans are also 30 to 50 percent more likely to have diabetes than their non-Hispanic white counterparts, even though Asian Americans are less likely to be overweight or obese according to standard measures (Hsu et al., 2015). Furthermore, rates of overweight and obesity prevalence among Asian American and NHPI children are growing at the fastest rate among all other racial and ethnic groups (Asian Pacific Partners for Empowerment, Advocacy and Leadership, 2014). This growing epidemic is especially prevalent among low-income children and NHPI children (Centers for Disease Control, 2015c; Shabbir et al., 2010). Indeed, income continues to be one of the most consistent predictors of health and disease (Minnesota Department of Health, 2014).

Mental health is also a major health concern for Asian Americans and NHPIs. Research shows a direct relationship between depression and chronic diseases including asthma, arthritis, cardiovascular disease, cancer, diabetes, and obesity (Chapman, Perry, and Strine, 2005). For example, Southeast Asian refugees who experienced severe trauma often suffer from high rates of posttraumatic stress disorder, cardiovascular disease, and diabetes (Wagner et al., 2013).

Yet Asian Americans and NHPIs are at increased risk for health problems as their mental health concerns often go unreported due to the stigma and shame associated with the topic. There is a critical lack of service providers who utilize an integrated approach to care and understand the role of culture, language, and historical trauma impacting Asian Americans and NHPIs. As a result, Asian Americans and NHPIs are the least likely of any group to seek mental health services (Abe-Kim et al., 2007). Yet the consequences of unreported mental health needs are dire; individuals with serious mental health conditions die twenty-five years earlier than the general population, and 70 percent of the deaths are due to co-occurring medical conditions such as cardiovascular disease and diabetes (Colton and Manderscheid, 2006).

Implications of 2040 Population Projections

The projections of Ong et al. show some significant estimated shifts in age, nativity, ethnicity, and sex among Asian Americans and NHPIs in 2040 compared to the population today. The proportion of foreign-born among Asian Americans will decrease from around 60 percent to 50 percent, while foreign-born Pacific Islanders will also experience a slight decrease from 20 to 16 percent (Ong and Ong, 2015). The decline in the proportion of foreign-born will be even more pronounced among younger generations, resulting in a generational divide. Only 40 percent of twenty-eight- to thirty-four-year-old Asian Americans and a little more than 10 percent of Pacific Islanders will be foreign-born in 2040, while their elder counterparts (aged sixty-five years and older) will be mostly foreign-born—around 85 percent amongst Asian Americans and 34 percent among Pacific Islanders (Ong and Ong, 2015).

Both the Asian American and NHPI inclusive populations will also see significant growth in the number of older adults. Asian Americans and NHPIs aged sixty and older will experience at least a 100 percent growth in the population by the year 2040 (ibid.).[5] The population of Asian American women aged sixty years and older will also increase nearly 60 percent, while NHPI women in that age group will grow by more than 50 percent (ibid.). Finally, the 2040 projections indicate the likelihood of a more multiracial society with an estimated 130 percent growth in multiracial Asian Americans.

These changes in the Asian American and NHPI population mean policy makers, health care, and other service providers and advocates must make policy and system improvements to increase health care access; strengthen the full spectrum of health care services including mental, behavioral, and preventive health and services tailored to foreign-born seniors; implement new information technologies; and plan for the future workforce needs in the country's health care system.

Access to Quality Health Care and Coverage

Public health insurance programs such as Medicaid, Medicare, and the Children's Health Insurance Program are critical sources of coverage for many Asian American and NHPI individuals and families. Approximately one in five Asian Americans and one in three NHPIs receive health insurance coverage through these programs (U.S. Census Bureau, 2013). The Affordable Care Act (ACA) increased access to these public insurance programs and created new health insurance marketplaces that provide subsidized private health insurance coverage for low- to moderate-income individuals. An estimated 1.9 million Asian Americans and NHPIs became eligible for the ACA's new health care coverage options when the marketplace first opened in 2014 (U.S. Department of Health and Human Services, Office of the Assistant Secretary for Planning and Evaluation and Office of Minority Health, 2014).

Yet, a significant portion of the Asian American and Pacific Islander community is excluded from participating in these programs due to their immigration status. For example, lawful permanent residents (LPRs), also known as "green card" holders, are barred from participating in the Medicaid program in most states until they have continuously resided in the United States for at least five years.

Even if eligible, many immigrants have trouble navigating the complex enrollment process and therefore remain uninsured (Action for Health Justice, 2014). For example, immigrant Asian Americans and Pacific Islanders over the age of sixty-five who meet the federal government's definition of "lawfully present" are eligible for some aspects of the Medicare program, while other Medicare features are limited to the narrower group of LPRs who have resided continuously in the United States for at least five years (National Immigration Law Center, 2013).

These restrictions create confusion and unnecessary barriers to enrollment, particularly among those who are LEP. Looking ahead, policy makers will need to respond to the continuing barriers facing immigrant Asian Americans and Pacific Islanders. As the population of foreign-born Asian Americans and Pacific Islanders increases dramatically among persons sixty years old and older, access to health insurance will be a critical issue. A rise in the number of uninsured seniors will translate into increased health care costs for all. However, removal of eligibility restrictions based on immigration status—such as the five-year bar for LPRs, the exclusion of young adults granted deferred action,[6] and categorical exemptions on individuals without lawful status—could help bend the cost curve and promote the public health goals of prevention and good health outcomes for all.

For the remaining uninsured, there are few options to seek non-emergency care. Those who are fortunate enough to have access to a federally qualified health center (FQHC) are able to receive health care services regardless of immigration status or ability to pay. Many FQHCs located in communities with a high concentration of Asian Americans and NHPIs also provide health care services in multiple Asian and Pacific Islander languages. Currently, nearly nine hundred thousand Asian Americans and NHPIs receive care at FQHCs (Association of Asian Pacific Community Health Organizations, 2015).

The ACA created an $11 billion Health Center Growth Fund to create new health center sites in medically underserved areas (MUAs) and to expand services. However, the current designations of MUAs and medically underserved populations do not adequately capture underserved Asian American and NHPI populations (Association of Asian Pacific Community Health Organizations, Asian & Pacific Islander American Health Forum, and Out of Many, One, 2010). Policy makers have an opportunity to release new designations to ensure a robust safety net is put into place for Asian American and NHPI communities in the future.

Health Care Delivery and Services

Health care providers, community-based organizations (CBOs), and hospital systems will need to plan for a growing population of older Asian Americans and NHPIs who are disproportionately LEP and immigrant. While health insurance coverage is a critical first step to improving individual health, access to health care alone is not enough. The quality of the health care services Asian American and NHPI consumers receive can affect the frequency of visits, openness to communicate, and likelihood of patient adherence between Asian Americans and NHPIs and their providers.

One of the most common factors affecting Asian American and NHPI patients' health care experience is language accessibility and cultural sensitivity. The Agency for Healthcare Research and Quality has long recognized that language barriers are a deterrent to seeking medical attention, and found the percentage of patients who reported not getting care as soon as they wanted was significantly lower for English speakers than non-English speakers (U.S. Department of Health and Human Services, Agency for Healthcare Research and Quality, 2014). Patients with both LEP and low health literacy—defined as not being able to read and understand content of health information—are also more likely to have poor health status (Sentell and Braun, 2012).

Asian Americans and NHPIs also underutilize health care services, and many subgroups lack a usual source of care. For example, 25 percent of Korean Americans and 18 percent of NHPIs lack a usual source of care compared to 10 percent of whites (Ponce et al., 2009). Studies have found Asian Americans were the least likely to report being very satisfied with the quality of their health care (Collins et al., 2002). An examination of California Health Interview Survey data also showed that Asian Americans were more likely to report lower quality of care (Sorkin, Ngo-Metzger, and De Alba 2010). Both studies surmised that English fluency and perceived discrimination had profound effects on Asian Americans during their clinical visit. As such, language accessibility and culturally appropriate care approaches are critical for many Asian Americans and NHPIs and should be considered essential in the delivery of services.

Health providers should anticipate an increased demand for women's health care services among Asian Americans and NHPIs. The Asian American and NHPI female population is expected to increase by nearly 50 to 60 percent over all age groups. Like other women, Asian American and NHPI women and girls will have many health care needs including life-saving preventive services and the full spectrum of reproductive health care. Asian American and NHPI women and girls report persistently low Pap screening rates, even though certain ethnic groups such as Vietnamese American women have the highest rate of cervical cancer for any racial or ethnic group in the United States (Ma et al., 2012). Breast cancer is also the most commonly diagnosed cancer for Asian American women, yet Asian American women aged fifty to seventy-four years are the least likely racial group to get a mammogram (Centers for Disease Control, 2012).

Over the next twenty-five years, an increasing number of Asian Americans and NHPIs, particularly among younger generations, will be multiracial, adding a layer of complexity to health screenings and services that have traditionally targeted mono-racial groups. Caring for multiracial Asian Americans and NHPIs will also mean fulfilling their mental and behavioral health needs. While research on mental and behavioral health in multiracial Asian Americans and NHPIs is limited, one survey review found significant increased risk of substance abuse by multiracial Asian Americans. In particular, multiracial Chinese American youth were more than four times more likely to use substances than their Chinese American counterparts, and multiracial Vietnamese Americans were nearly four times more likely to use substances than other Vietnamese American youth (Price et al., 2002). One can infer that such behavioral health risk factors will become more prevalent among multiracial Asian Americans and NHPIs in 2040.

While policy makers, health providers, and advocates will need to be responsive to the demographic shifts among Asian Americans and NHPIs, they will also need to continue to address the health care service needs of children; lesbian, gay, bisexual, and transgender (LGBT) individuals; and other vulnerable populations. For example, LGBT individuals often experience stigma in their communities and from their health providers, leading to adverse health outcomes. Community education, outreach, and interventions are also needed to address the high percentage of underinsured Asian American and NHPI children and the underutilization of preventive services among Asian American and NHPI women. Studies have shown that several subgroups of Asian American women are the least likely among all racial groups to receive early and adequate prenatal care, putting mothers and their babies at increased risk of low-birth weight, preterm birth, and infant mortality (Asian & Pacific Islander American Health Forum, 2012b).

Utilizing New Information Technologies

Along with the ACA, the American Recovery and Reinvestment Act of 2009 (ARRA) provided resources and incentives to adopt and integrate electronic health records (EHRs) into health care systems. ARRA's new federal dollars in EHRs represented a unique opportunity for providers to better monitor and evaluate the efficacy of care, utility of services, and correlate interventions to patients' health outcomes. As a result, the Association of Asian Pacific Community Health Organizations and its member health centers launched an initiative to use EHRs to establish a national data warehouse on Asian American and NHPI health. The hope is that utilization of new technologies to create the data repository will improve the health and wellness of Asian Americans and NHPIs on a population scale through (1) the disaggregation of dozens of Asian American and NHPI racial subgroups and more than two dozen respective languages; (2) national standardization of enabling services, critical nonclinical services that enhance access, continuity, and quality of care; (3) the integration and collection of nationally standardized social determinants of health data; and (4) better care management and reduction of total cost of care.

Health care providers are rapidly adopting new technologies and digital tools to connect patients and providers outside of the examination room. These advancements in the field of health information technology (HIT) hold great promise in improving access to care and quality. However, these technologies and the systems that support them are not equally accessible to many communities of color, older populations, rural communities, or among individuals who do not speak English well (California Pan-Ethnic Health Network et al., 2013). Thus, providers must be mindful that new HIT tools do not further exacerbate or deter existing service gaps in underserved communities. New innovations, such as mobile applications on smartphones to increase language access, are needed to meet the needs of Asian Americans and NPHIs in 2040.

Creating an effective and technologically integrated health care delivery system capable of improving health outcomes among Asian Americans and NHPIs will also require standardized systems of collecting, monitoring, and reporting disaggregated data. Asian Americans and NHPIs are not a monolithic group, and current data collection and reporting practices that aggregate Asian Americans and NHPIs mask existing inequities. Identifying immigration status—one of the greatest determinants of health insurance coverage and access—in a safe, secure, and trusted fashion is also a particular data collection challenge. As Asian American and NHPI communities continue to grow and become increasingly diverse, it will be important to understand particular health access and outcome challenges related to other demographic factors such as sex, primary spoken/written language, gender identity, and sexual orientation.

Health Care Workforce

The U.S. health care system already faces challenges recruiting and training Asian American and NHPI bilingual and/or bicultural professional and allied health care workers, particularly in underserved areas. With a rapidly growing Asian American and NHPI population expected in just more than a generation, providers, hospital systems, FQHCs, and other health care delivery institutions will experience an increased demand for interpreting services, translated materials, and culturally appropriate approaches when caring for Asian American and NHPI consumers. Multiracial Asian Americans and NHPIs will also benefit from health care providers, workers, and services that recognize the unique needs of individuals who identify with more than one race or ethnicity.

Providers must plan for the increased number of Asian American and NHPI seniors seeking elder care services in 2040. On a per capita basis, the elderly have the most hospital inpatient days, outpatient visits, and emergency department visits (U.S. Department of Health and Human Services, Health Services and Services Administration, 2003).

Relative to the nonelderly, they also have more home health visits per capita and are more likely to be in a long-term care facility. As such, new and existing recruitment and training programs, especially for members of allied health teams such as mid-level providers (e.g., nurse practitioners and physician assistants), physical and occupational therapists, and community and home health workers, are critically needed to ensure that an ethnically, culturally, and linguistically diverse public health, health, and health care workforce and infrastructure is in place by 2040.

Moreover, while the projections of Ong et al. do not show the geographic distribution of Asian American and NHPI population growth, recent U.S. Census data show several states in the South and Midwest are experiencing the fastest Asian American and NHPI growth in the country (Asian Americans Advancing Justice, 2011). Looking ahead, the Asian American and NHPI population in these regions will likely continue to grow and there will be increasing demand for health and social services that can meet their physical, mental, and behavioral health needs. Populations that reside in rural areas will face even greater challenges; many rural areas and Pacific jurisdictions are designated as physician shortage areas.

CBOs can play an effective role in addressing some of the workforce shortage issues, particularly within immigrant, linguistically isolated, and rural communities. CBOs either provide or help facilitate the delivery of culturally and linguistically appropriate health and social services to community members who are not connected to "mainstream" service programs. CBO staff are trusted members of the communities they serve and act as patient advocates, care coordinators, and outreach workers. These organizations have a unique set of knowledge and expertise on underserved communities and can be a valuable partner to care providers, health care systems, and other local institutions.

The ACA highlights the importance of integrated care approaches that address the physical, mental, and behavioral health needs of this country. Yet, there are differing opinions as to the meaning of "integrated care" and many challenges in the development and implementation of integrated models of care (Kodner and Spreeuwenberg, 2002). The definition of *integrated care* will have long-lasting implications on how providers are trained in the physical, mental, and behavioral health arenas; how treatment plans and intervention strategies are developed; what service delivery partners are identified; and the location of services and sharing of medical records. For example, while the federal government does not prohibit same-day billing for physical and mental health services by the same provider on the same day, only twenty-eight states currently allow for same-day billing (Reynolds, 2012). There is also a need to conduct research on best practices models of integrated care in both health care clinics and CBOs to assess core competencies across disciplines, utilization of paraprofessionals, and investigate systems issues impacting both (Ida, SooHoo, and Chapa, 2012).

Toward a New Vision of Health Equity

The Asian American and NHPI population in the United States will grow and evolve in unprecedented ways over the next decade. The changes in the population's demographics will challenge current and traditional approaches to how health workers provide physical and mental health services, as well as how researchers monitor health care quality and utilization among Asian Americans and NHPIs. Future quality measures will need to include standards for cultural and linguistic appropriateness, while existing analyses that focus singularly on biological traits such as race, ethnicity, or sex will be too limiting.

Instead, anticipating future trends will require a reevaluation of structural barriers and other socioeconomic factors. This approach, also known as a "health determinants" framework, takes into account non-clinical conditions, such as income, social supports, and the physical and social environments where a person lives, works, learns, or plays (McGovern, Miller, and Hughes-Cromwick, 2014). For example, individuals and families with higher incomes are more likely to live in neighborhoods and communities with full-service grocery stores and safe spaces for outdoor activities such as playgrounds and parks. Thus, individuals living in these communities are more likely to live longer, healthier lives compared to those who live in low-income communities that lack these basic living conditions (Minnesota Department of Health, 2014). Racial and ethnic minorities including Asian Americans and NHPIs are more likely than whites to live in low-income communities (Joint Center for Economic and Political Studies, 2013). Adopting a health determinants analysis to measure health outcomes and health care quality may prove useful as Asian Americans and NHPIs as an identity group become increasingly multiracial and experience greater generational differences based on immigration status, English proficiency, and geography. It is important to recognize that this diversification will also take place among other communities of color. As such, achieving Asian American and NHPI health equity will depend on our ability to collaborate on health promotion efforts across all racial and ethnic groups.

The need for a broader framework that recognizes the multiple factors and varied lived experiences of individuals and their families is especially acute within the Asian American and NHPI population. In most federal research and household surveys, Asian Americans and NHPIs are often grouped together in one or two race categories, yet there is no singular, defining Asian American or NHPI experience. Grouping Asian Americans and NHPIs together may serve to provide statistical power, however, it masks the rich and varied cultures and immigration histories that constitute the dozens of ethnic subgroups that make up Asian American and NHPI communities. Similarly, a health determinants approach that contextualizes the social, institutional, community, and individual factors associated with physical, mental, and behavioral health outcomes will be more useful for identifying effective prevention and intervention strategies for the Asian American and NHPI population in 2040.

Some efforts are already underway to actualize a health determinants framework through public policy. Just a few months after the enactment of the ACA, a group of advocates representing a broad cross-section of disease, population, and professional health organizations worked with members of the "Tri-Caucus" to revise and reintroduce the Health Equity and Accountability Act of 2011 (HEAA), the most sweeping health equity bill to date (U.S. Congresswoman Barbara Lee, 2014).[7] Building on the ACA's historic expansion of health insurance coverage to millions of uninsured, HEAA provides a road map for addressing a range of mental, behavioral, environmental, and physical health determinants (Asian & Pacific Islander American Health Forum, 2011b). For example, the bill focuses on ensuring that a full range of culturally and linguistically appropriate health care and public health services are available and accessible to all; creates additional pipeline and training opportunities for minority-serving professional and allied health care workers; and supports community-based prevention efforts to address a range of disease-specific, mental, and behavioral health issues facing communities of color and other barriers such as immigration status, age, disability, obesity, sexual orientation, gender identity, and LEP (Asian & Pacific Islander American Health Forum, 2012c). The bill was introduced by Representative Barbara Lee with eighty-three cosponsors. A Senate companion bill was introduced in 2012, and HEAA was subsequently reintroduced in the House in 2014.

Legislative efforts and policies such as HEAA must be enacted soon to ensure health care systems and other institutions can accommodate future Asian American, NHPI, and other population groups with diverse and complex needs. Federal, state, and local governments can also take steps today to implement the principles and policy solutions outlined in HEAA and other policy tools to redesign their health and social service infrastructure to meet the needs of Asian Americans and NHPIs in 2040. For example, state and county public health departments could adopt in their health surveys some of HEAA's recommended demographic categories to capture information about residents' ethnicity, primary language, gender identity, and sexual orientation. Similarly, public health departments could work with other agencies to design and implement a set of metrics for measuring and tracking health determinants across a cross-section of socioeconomic factors. What's clear is that transformations are needed, and a continuation of the status quo will not adequately propel Asian American and NHPI communities to healthier outcomes in 2040.

Conclusion

Implementation of the ACA is still underway nearly six years after its historic passage. While the long-term effects are unknown, the short-term impacts of expanded health care coverage, lower premium costs, no-cost preventive care, and other important investments have benefited millions of Americans, including Asian Americans and NHPIs (Burwell, 2015). Health insurance coverage is certainly a universal need in the United States, however health conditions and outcomes among Asian Americans and NHPIs will not improve with mere access to health coverage. Policy makers, public health departments, and health care institutions must implement reforms that recognize the growing and diverse physical, mental, environmental, and behavioral health care needs of Asian Americans, NHPIs, and all Americans through a health determinants lens. With the U.S. Supreme Court's decisions to uphold a key aspect of the ACA, policy makers can finally shift from defending the health reform law to improving it. Inaction will merely exacerbate existing health and health care inequities among Asian Americans and NHPIs, leading to increased costs and burdens on the U.S. health care system in 2040. To achieve our vision for 2040, Asian Americans and NHPIs must advance public health and health equity.

Acknowledgments

The authors would like to thank Edward Tepporn for his editing support.

Notes

1. The 2040 projections reflect the Asian American and NHPI populations in the fifty states, and do not include individuals residing in the U.S. Pacific Island jurisdictions.

2. The authors adopt the definition of health utilized by the World Health Organization: "Health is a state of complete physical, mental and social well-being and not merely the absence of disease or infirmity. The term 'health and health care inequities' refers to systemic, environmental and structural disparities affecting particular population group(s)" (see Trinh-Shevrin, Islam, Nadkarni, 2015).

3. The term underinsured refers to individuals enrolled in a health plan that does not adequately cover their medical expenses (see Gold, 2009).

4. Defined as having an annual income of $11,770 or less for an individual according to the 2015 federal poverty level.

5. The size of the percent change is the result of small numbers in 2015.

6. The exclusion would also apply to future individuals granted administrative relief through President Obama's executive actions expanding deferred action for young adults and creating a new deferred action program for the parents of U.S. citizens or LPRs. As of this writing, these programs have not been implemented due to pending litigation.

7. The "Tri-Caucus" is comprised of the Congressional Asian Pacific American Caucus, Congressional Hispanic Caucus, and Congressional Black Caucus. The Healthcare Taskforce chairs of each caucus rotate as the lead sponsor of HEAA during each congressional session.

References

Abe-Kim, J., Takeuchi, D. T., Hong, S., Zane, N., Sue, S., Spencer, M. S., and M. Alegría. 2007. "Use of Mental Health–Related Services among Immigrant and US-Born Asian Americans: Results from the National Latino and Asian American Study." *American Journal of Public Health* 97(1): 91–8.

Action for Health Justice. 2014. "Lessons Learned on Outreach, Education and Enrollment for Asian American, Native Hawaiian and Pacific Islander Communities." http://www.apiahf.org/resources/resources-database/improving-road-aca-coverage-lessons-learned-outreach-education-and-enro (accessed June 15, 2015).

Asian Americans Advancing Justice. 2011. "A Community of Contrasts: Asian Americans in the United States 2011." http://www.advancingjustice.org/sites/default/files/Community_of_Contrast.pdf (accessed June 15, 2015).

Asian & Pacific Islander American Health Forum. 2012a. "The Impact of Health Care Reform on Health Coverage for Asian Americans, Native Hawaiians and Pacific Islanders." http://www.apiahf.org/sites/default/files/PA-Factsheet0613-2012.pdf (accessed June 15, 2015).

———. 2012b. "Maternal and Child Health of Asian Americans, Native Ha-

waiians and Pacific Islanders." http://www.apiahf.org/sites/default/files/
APIAHF%20Maternal%20and%20Child%20Health%20of%20AANHPI.pdf
(accessed June 15, 2015).

———. 2012c. "HEAA of 2012 Request to Co-sponsor Letter." http://www.api-
ahf.org/sites/default/files/HEAA%20of%202012%20Request%20to%20co-
sponsor%20final.pdf (accessed June 15, 2015).

———. 2011a. "Coverage Gains for Asian American, Native Hawaiian and Pacific Islander Children under Health Care Reform." http://www.apiahf.org/
sites/default/files/PA-factsheet09-2011_0.pdf (accessed June 15, 2015).

———. 2011b. "HEAA One Pager." http://www.apiahf.org/sites/default/
files/HEAA%20One%20pager.pdf (accessed June 15, 2015).

Asian Pacific Partners for Empowerment, Advocacy and Leadership. 2014.
"Health Disparities Faced by Asian Americans, Native Hawaiians and Pacific Islanders." http://www.appealforcommunities.org/wp-content/up-
loads/2014/06/4761_HealthDisparitiesFacedbyAANHPI_FactSheet_v.3.pdf
(accessed June 15, 2015).

Association of Asian Pacific Community Health Organizations. 2015. "AAP-
CHO Helps Kick-off First Ever AAPI Nexus Journal Issue on Community
Health Centers, March 17, 2015." http://www.aapcho.org/press-release/
aapcho-helps-kick-off-first-ever-aapi-nexus-journal-issue-on-community-
health-centers/ (accessed June 15, 2015).

Association of Asian Pacific Community Health Organizations, Asian & Pacific Islander American Health Forum, and Out of Many, One. 2010. Comment
letter on Notice of Intent to Form Negotiated Rulemaking Committee, 75
Fed. Reg. 26167, et seq. http://www.aapcho.org/resources_db/comments-
on-notice-of-intent-to-form-negotiated-rulemaking-committee/ (accessed
June 15, 2015).

Burwell, S. 2015. "HHS Secretary: Affordable Care Act Is Working." USA Today, 19 February. http://www.usatoday.com/story/opinion/2015/02/19/
aca-achievements-burwell/23672239/ (accessed June 15, 2015).

California Pan-Ethnic Health Network, Asian & Pacific Islander American
Health Forum, National Council of La Raza, and Consumers Union. 2013.
"Equity in the Digital Age: How Health Information Technology Can Reduce Disparities." http://cpehn.org/sites/default/files/resource_files/eq-
uityinthedigitalage2013_0.pdf (accessed June 15, 2015).

Centers for Disease Control and Prevention. 2015a. "Surveillance for Viral Hepatitis—United States, 2013." Viral Hepatitis—Statistics and Surveillance.
http://www.cdc.gov/hepatitis/statistics/2013surveillance/commentary.
htm (accessed September 29, 2015).

———. 2015b. "Diabetes Among Asians and Native Hawaiians or other Pacific Islanders—United States, 2011-2014." MMWR Morbidity and Mortality
Weekly Report. http://www.cdc.gov/mmwr/pdf/wk/mm6445.pdf (accessed March 31, 2016).

———. 2015c. "Prevalence of Childhood Obesity in the United States, 2011–

2012." Childhood Obesity Facts. http://www.cdc.gov/obesity/data/childhood.html (accessed September 29, 2015).

———. 2013. "Reported Tuberculosis in the United States, 2012." U.S. Department of Health and Human Services. October. http://www.cdc.gov/tb/statistics/reports/2012/pdf/report2012.pdf (accessed June 15, 2015).

———. 2012. "Breast Cancer Screening Rates." Breast Cancer. http://www.cdc.gov/cancer/breast/statistics/screening.htm (accessed September 29, 2015).

Chapman, D. P., Perry, G. S., and T. W. Strine. 2005. "The Vital Link between Chronic Disease and Depressive Disorders." *Preventing Chronic Disease* [serial online] 2(1). http://www.cdc.gov/pcd/issues/2005/jan/04_0066.htm (accessed June 15, 2015).

Collins, K. S., Hughes, D. L., Doty, M. M., Ives, B. L., Edwards, J. N., and K. Tenney. 2002. "Diverse Communities, Common Concerns: Assessing Health Care Quality for Minority Americans: Findings from the Commonwealth Fund 2001 Health Care Quality Survey." March. http://www.commonwealthfund.org/usr_doc/collins_diversecommun_523.pdf?section=4039 (accessed June 15, 2015).

Colton, C. W., and R. W. Manderscheid. 2006. "Congruencies in Increased Mortality Rates, Years of Potential Life Lost, and Causes of Death among Public Mental Health Clients in Eight States." *Preventing Chronic Disease* 3(2). http://www.ncbi.nlm.nih.gov/pmc/articles/PMC1563985/pdf/PCD32A42.pdf (accessed June 15, 2015).

Empowering Pacific Islander Communities and Asian Americans Advancing Justice. 2014. "A Community of Contrasts: Native Hawaiians and Pacific Islanders in the United States 2014." http://empoweredpi.org/wp-content/uploads/2014/06/A_Community_of_Contrasts_NHPI_US_2014-1.pdf (accessed June 15, 2015).

Gold, Jenny. 2009. "The Underinsurance Problem Explained." *Kaiser Health News*, 29 September. http://khn.org/news/underinsured-explainer/ (accessed June 15, 2015).

Hsu, W. C., Araneta, M. R. G., Kanaya, A. M., Chiang, J. L., and W. Fujimoto. 2015. "BMI Cut Points to Identify At-Risk Asian Americans for Diabetes Type 2 Screening." *Diabetes Care* 38(1): 150–8. http://care.diabetesjournals.org/content/38/1/150.full (accessed June 15, 2015).

Ida, D. J., SooHoo, J., and T. Chapa. 2012. "Integrated Care for Asian American, Native Hawaiian and Pacific Islander Communities: A Blueprint for Action: Consensus Statement and Recommendations." Rockville, MD: U.S. Department of Health and Human Services, Office of Minority Health. http://www.integration.samhsa.gov/workforce/Integrated_Care_for_AANHPI_Communities 1_23_12_Blue_II pdf (accessed June 15, 2015).

Joint Center for Political and Economic Studies. 2013. "Place Matters: Advancing Health Equity." http://nationalcollaborative.org/sites/default/files/JC013_Success_040213_revised-R3%20%283%29.pdf (accessed March 2, 2016).

Kodner, D. L., and C. Spreeuwenberg. 2002. "Integrated Care: Meaning, Logic, Applications, and Implications—A Discussion Paper." *International Journal of Integrated Care* 2: e12. http://www.ncbi.nlm.nih.gov/pmc/articles/PMC1480401/ (accessed June 15, 2015).

Ma, G., Fang, C., Feng, Z., Tan, Y., Gao, W., Ge, S., and C. Nguyen. 2012. "Correlates of Cervical Cancer Screening among Vietnamese American Women." *Infectious Diseases in Obstetrics and Gynecology* 2012. http://www.hindawi.com/journals/idog/2012/617234/ (accessed June 15, 2015).

McGovern, L., Miller, G., and P. Hughes-Cromwick. 2014. "Health Policy Brief." *Health Affairs*, 21 August. http://healthaffairs.org/healthpolicybriefs/brief_pdfs/healthpolicybrief_123.pdf (accessed June 15, 2015).

Minnesota Department of Health. 2014. White Paper on Income and Health. http://www.health.state.mn.us/divs/opa/2014incomeandhealth.pdf (accessed September 24, 2015).

National Coalition for Asian Pacific American Community Development. 2013. "Spotlight on Asian American and Pacific Islander Poverty: A Demographic Profile." http://nationalcapacd.org/spotlight-asian-american-and-pacific-islander-poverty-demographic-profile (accessed June 15, 2015).

National Immigration Law Center. 2013. Table: Overview of Immigrant Eligibility for Federal Programs. http://www.nilc.org/table_ovrw_fedprogs.html (accessed June 15, 2015).

Ong, Jonathan, Ong, Paul, and Elena Ong. 2016. "The Future of Asian America in 2040." *AAPI Nexus Journal: Policy, Practice, and Community* 14(1): 14–29.

Ong, Paul, and Elena Ong. 2015. "One-in-Ten: The Future of AAs and PIs 2015–2040." UCLA Center for the Study of Inequality, PowerPoint slides.

Pew Research Center. 2012. *The Rise of Asian Americans*. Washington, DC: Pew Research Center.

Ponce N., Tseng W., Ong P., et al. 2009. "The State of Asian American, Native Hawaiian and Pacific Islander Health in California Report." April. http://www.cdph.ca.gov/programs/Documents/AANHPI_report_April2009.pdf (accessed June 15, 2015).

Price, R. K., Risk, N. K., Wong, M. M., and Klingle, R. S. 2002. "Substance Use and Abuse by Asian Americans and Pacific Islanders: Preliminary Results from Four National Epidemiologic Studies." *Public Health Reports* 117 (Suppl. 1): S39–S50. http://www.ncbi.nlm.nih.gov/pmc/articles/PMC1913701/ (accessed June 15, 2015).

Reynolds, K. 2012. "Footing the Bill for Integrated Care." *eSolutions Newsletter.* SAMHSA-HRSA Center for Integrated Health Solutions. http://www.integration.samhsa.gov/about-us/esolutions-newsletter/june-2012 (accessed June 15, 2015).

Sentell, T., and K. L. Braun. 2012. "Low Health Literacy, Limited English Proficiency, and Health Status in Asians, Latinos, and Other Racial/Ethnic Groups in California." *Journal of Health Communication* 17 (Suppl. 3): 82–99. http://www.tandfonline.com/doi/pdf/10.1080/10810730.2012.712621 (accessed June 15, 2015).

Shabbir, S., Kwan, D., Wang, M., Shih, M., and P. Simon. 2010. "Asians and Pacific Islanders and the Growing Childhood Obesity Epidemic." *Ethnicity and Disease* 20: 129–35. http://www.hypnoanalysis.eshonline.ishib.org/journal/20-2/ethn-20-02-129.pdf (accessed June 15, 2015).

Sorkin, D. H., Ngo-Metzger, Q., and I. De Alba. 2010. "Racial/Ethnic Discrimination in Health Care: Impact on Perceived Quality of Care." *Journal of General Internal Medicine* 25(5): 390–6. http://link.springer.com/article/10.1007/s11606-010-1257-5/fulltext.html (accessed June 15, 2015).

Trinh-Shevrin, Chau, Islam, Nadia S., and Smiti Nadkarni. 2015. "Defining an Integrative Approach for Health Promotion and Disease Prevention: A Population Health Equity Framework." *Journal of Health Care for the Poor and Underserved* 2: 146–63.

U.S. Census Bureau. 2015a. Current Population Reports. "Projections of the Size and Composition of the U.S. Population: 2014 to 2060." https://www.census.gov/content/dam/Census/library/publications/2015/demo/p25-1143.pdf (accessed January 15, 2016).

———. 2015b. "Population Division: Annual Estimates of the Resident Population by Sex, Race Alone or in Combination, and Hispanic Origin for the United States, States, and Counties: April 1, 2010 to July 1, 2014." http://factfinder.census.gov/faces/tableservices/jsf/pages/productview.xhtml?src=bkmk (accessed June 15, 2015).

———. 2013. "American Community Survey 1-Year Estimates for Asian Alone and Native Hawaiian or Other Pacific Islander Estimates." Table S0201. http://factfinder.census.gov/faces/tableservices/jsf/pages/productview.xhtml?src=bkmk (accessed June 15, 2015).

U.S. Congresswoman Barbara Lee. 2014. "Tri-Caucus Members Introduce the Health Equity and Accountability Act of 2014." Press Release. http://lee.house.gov/news/press-releases/tri-caucus-members-introduce-the-health-equity-and-accountability-act-of-2014 (accessed June 15, 2015).

U.S. Department of Health and Human Services. Agency for Healthcare Research and Quality (AHRQ). 2014. "National Healthcare Disparities Report 2013." May 2014. Available at: http://www.ahrq.gov/research/findings/nhqrdr/nhdr13/2013nhdr.pdf (accessed June 15, 2015).

———. Health Resources and Services Administration. 2003. "Changing Demographics: Implications for Physicians, Nurses and Health Workers." http://www.nachc.org/client/documents/clinical/Clinical_Workforce_Changing_Demographics.pdf (accessed June 15, 2015).

———. Office of the Assistant Secretary for Planning and Evaluation and Office of Minority Health. 2014. "Eligible Uninsured Asian Americans, Native Hawaiians and Pacific Islanders: 8 in 10 Could Receive Health Insurance Marketplace Tax Credits, Medicaid or CHIP." http://aspe.hhs.gov/health/reports/2014/UninsuredAANHPI/rb_UninsuredAANHPI.pdf (accessed June 15, 2015).

Wagner, J., Burke, G., Kuoch, T., Scully, M., Armeli, S., and T. V. Rajan. 2013. "Trauma, Healthcare Access, and Health Outcomes among Southeast Asian Refugees in Connecticut." *Journal of Immigrant Minority Health* 15(6): 1065–72. http://www.ncbi.nlm.nih.gov/pubmed/?term=wagner+burke+southe ast (accessed June 15, 2015).

Zong, J., and J. Batalova. 2015. "The Limited English Proficient Population in the United States." *Migration Policy Institute*, 8 July. http://www.migrationpolicy.org/article/limited-english-proficient-population-united-states#Age, Race, and Ethnicity (accessed September 24, 2015).

PRISCILLA HUANG, JD, is an independent consultant and works with various clients in the nonprofit and governmental sectors. She was the former Senior Director of Impact Strategies at the Asian & Pacific Islander American Health Forum (APIAHF), where she served as its primary policy strategist and supervised the organization's policy, government relations, communications, and research staff. Prior to APIAHF, Priscilla served as the policy and programs director at the National Asian Pacific American Women's Forum where she oversaw the federal policy advocacy and government relations for their immigrant rights, antitrafficking, and reproductive justice programs. Priscilla has served on several boards and advisory committees and has been recognized for her leadership by the White House, National Immigration Law Center, the Congressional Black Caucus Health Braintrust, Families USA, and others.

KATHY KO CHIN is president and chief executive officer of the Asian & Pacific Islander American Health Forum, a national health justice organization that influences policy, mobilizes communities, and strengthens programs and organizations to improve the health of Asian Americans, Native Hawaiians, and Pacific Islanders. Kathy has worked in senior management positions in community-based and philanthropic organizations throughout her thirty-five-year career.

JEFFREY B. CABALLERO, MPH, is Executive Director of the Association of Asian and Pacific Community Health Organizations (AAPCHO) and has been with the organization since 1993. In this capacity, Mr. Caballero advocates for programs and policies that increase access to high-quality, comprehensive community health care services that are culturally and linguistically appropriate. He has overall authority for all AAPCHO programs, finances, and operations and serves as chief spokesperson for the organization.

DJ IDA, PhD, received her doctorate in clinical psychology and has more than thirty-five years of experience working with Asian American and Native Hawaiian and Pacific Islander communities and currently serves as the Executive Director of NAAPIMHA. She has been a strong advocate for mental health and focuses her attention on raising awareness, eliminating stigma, and improving overall quality of life for Asian Americans and Native Hawaiian and Pacific Islanders , recognizing the strong role mental health plays.

MYRON DEAN QUON, Esq., is the Executive Director of National Asian Pacific American Families Against Substance Abuse, a national nonprofit advocate that addresses substance use disorders and other behavioral addictions in Asian American, Native Hawaiian, and Pacific Islander communities through research, advocacy, education, and capacity building. Mr. Quon leads its programs including advocacy for language access and cultural competency, problem gambling trainings, and community prevention programs focused on alcohol, tobacco, and other drugs.

aapi nexus Vol. 14, No. 1 (Spring 2016): 130-143

Practitioner Essay

Asian American Pacific Islander Environmental Leadership for 2040

Charles Lee

Abstract

Climate change is an unprecedented issue that shapes the era in which we now live. Asian Americans and Pacific Islanders (AAPIs) have a stake in environmental justice because AAPIs are disproportionately impacted by climate change. This essay examines how the climate crisis affects AAPIs, and provides examples of the leadership AAPIs have demonstrated to address climate and social equity concerns. These leadership lessons are relevant to the leadership role that AAPIs can play now and in the future, for 2040 and beyond.

Introduction

The year 2040 represents an important moment of passage for Asian Americans and Pacific Islanders (AAPIs). That year is when AAPIs will become one-tenth of the population in the United States. It is challenging to look ahead twenty-five years in any area and say something precise. But it is particularly challenging for an area such as AAPIs and the environment, for which there has been generally very little systematic attention. However, one can say for sure that the issues at the intersection of the natural, built, and social environments will have profound impacts during the next quarter century for AAPIs. These issues range from environmental and occupational health, community development and gentrification, to climate change. AAPIs should pay attention to them because they will be an integral part of our lives in increasingly pervasive ways.

I have the distinct honor of being asked to offer my reflections about AAPI environmental leadership challenges and opportunities for 2040 because of my role in helping to give birth to the environmental justice movement in the United States. I will do so through the lens of climate justice, which focuses on the reality that communities of color, the poor, and indigenous peoples bear the greatest burden of the climate crisis. Climate justice addresses the ways in which climate, environmental degradation, and racial, social, and economic inequities are intertwined.

In this essay, I will examine how the climate crisis affects AAPIs, particularly the little known plight of Pacific Islanders. I will then highlight two remarkable examples of how AAPIs have played a leadership role in regard to climate issues. Both case studies speak to unprecedented issues that will more and more shape the era in which we now live. The first is the response of the Vietnamese community to the devastation of Hurricane Katrina in the New Orleans East section of New Orleans. The second is AAPI leadership in conceptualization, passage, and implementation of California's landmark Senate Bill 535 (SB 535), which designated that at least 25 percent of the proceeds from the state's Greenhouse Gas Reduction Fund must benefit disadvantaged communities. Throughout, I will draw some lessons for environmental leadership over the next twenty-five years.

AAPI Environmentalism and the Climate Crisis

In our introductory essay for the groundbreaking UCLA *AAPI Nexus Journal* special issue on AAPI environmentalism, Julie Sze, Paul Ong, and I defined *environmentalism* broadly to include the nexus between people and natural resources, environmentalism, and environmental justice. We said that "Asian American environmentalism in praxis tells us important stories of our age: about what counts as environmentalism for AAPI (including immigrant and refugee communities in the United States) within a global context of population migration, and the movement of pollution across international spaces; what communities are doing to address the myriad environmental problems and pollution exposures they face; and how these populations are at the cutting edge of environmental policy, especially in community-based health research and policy" (Sze, Ong, and Lee, 2013, p. 83).

Pope Francis's 2015 encyclical *Laudato Si* was a worldwide wake-up call to help humanity understand the destruction that man is rendering to the environment and his fellow man (Pope Francis, 2015). While addressing the environment directly, the document's scope is broader in many ways as it looks at not only man's effect on the environment, but also the many philosophical, theological, and cultural factors that threaten the relationships of man to nature and man to each other in various circumstances (Cotter, 2015). It is a message for people of all faiths, all backgrounds, and all times.

Pope Francis called climate change one of the "principal challenges facing humanity in our day." He warned that it is a "global problem with grave implications: environmental, social, economic, political and for the distribution of goods and "if present trends continue, this century may well witness extraordinary climate change and an unprecedented destruction of ecosystems, with serious consequences for all of us" (Pope Francis, 2015, p. 20). However, the *Washington Post* noted that the most radical part of Pope Francis's message wasn't about climate change. *Laudato Si*'s "far-reaching impact could be owed to another aspect of the document, which ties together all of the environmental concerns it will address: its focus on environmental justice" (Harvey, 2015). Climate change's worst impact "will probably be felt by developing countries in coming decades. Many of the poor live in areas particularly affected by phenomena related to warming, and their means of subsistence are largely dependent on natural reserves and ecosystemic services such as agriculture, fishing and forestry" (Hale, 2015).

Climate Change Threats to the Pacific Islands

While these words apply to all people, they describe perils of particular gravity for Pacific Islanders and other indigenous populations. According to the Pacific Islands Regional Climate Assessment (2015), a collaborative effort aimed at assessing the climate change indicators, impacts, and adaptive capacity of the Hawaiian archipelago and the U.S.-Affiliated Pacific Islands, evidence suggests many ways in which climate change poses a threat to human and natural communities in the Pacific Islands region. Multiple impacts are forecast, including decreased freshwater supplies; increased coastal flooding and erosion; increased ocean acidification and changing ocean chemistry; decline of open-ocean fisheries; and increased risk of extinctions. Threats to the traditional lifestyles of indigenous communities may include destruction of coastal artifacts and structures, reduced availability of traditional food sources and subsistence fisheries, and the loss of the land base that supports Pacific Island cultures. These losses will make it difficult for Pacific Island communities to sustain their connection to a defined place and their unique set of customs, beliefs, and languages.

Ultimately, migration may be the only option for many Pacific Islanders. Mounting threats to food and water security; infrastructure; and public health and safety will lead to human migration from low islands to high islands and continental sites (Pacific Islands Regional Climate Assessment, 2015). This is not just a phenomenon of the future. Worldwide, an International Displacement Monitoring Center report (2014) estimated twenty-two million people were displaced by natural disasters in 2013, and it pointed out that Pacific Island countries are disproportionately affected by disasters and the displacement they cause. These facts underscore why climate change impacts in the Pacific Islands must be addressed in the present, as well as in the future. Our global carbon footprint, one that Pacific Islanders have done little to cause, are already at dangerous levels. Its effects are being felt already and will only be worse in 2040 unless we seize the moment to control greenhouse gas emissions now.

Vietnamese Community Response to Hurricane Katrina

In the wake of the devastation wrought by Hurricane Katrina in 2005, the Village de l'Est Vietnamese community provided the nation with a remarkable story of return, rebuilding, and rebirth (see Figure 1). It continues to inspire people of all backgrounds and provides lessons on the important role of community social capital and resilience. Hurricane Katrina etched into the American consciousness not just the horrific images of destruction resulting from climate change, but it also reminded us about how persistent racial segregation and social exclusion have made certain communities more vulnerable to climate change impacts. This historical context has made the story of Mary Queen of Vietnam Church in Village de l'Est all the more noteworthy. One of the first communities to recover and rebuild, Village de l'Est, as New Orleans City Council Member Cynthia Williard Lewis said, can serve as "a model for other communities" (Leong et al., 2007).

Father Vien Nguyen, pastor of the Mary Queen of Vietnam Church, spearheaded the efforts of Village de l'Est community residents to return to their homes and rebuild their lives. Because of the tight-knit nature of this immigrant community, he had information on the locations where his parishioners had dispersed. Armed with this information, he traveled throughout the country to find his parishioners and facilitate their return. "My people were in California, Georgia, Florida, Washington, Minnesota, Michigan, [Texas,] and the Carolinas. They even went so far as New Hampshire and Connecticut." The pastor asked available council and hamlet representatives to meet in Houston to plan for the return to the parish as soon as permission was granted for people to reenter New Orleans. According to Nguyen, on October 5, 2005, the first day people could return to the city to begin the cleanup, more than three hundred parish members did so (Leong et al., 2007).

Figure 1. Map of Village de l'Est, Home to the Vietnamese American Community in New Orleans East

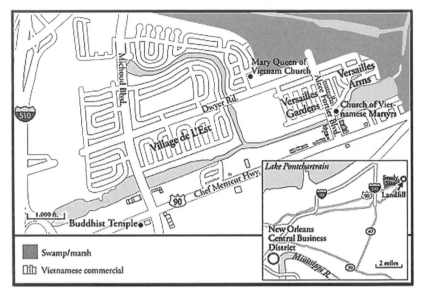

Source: Leong et al., 2007

One of the first things Nguyen did was to organize his parishioners to advocate for the resumption of basic services and to ensure the community's voice in the rebuilding process. In November 2005, Nguyen organized residents, mostly home owners returning to New Orleans East, in a petition drive to demand electricity and water. He submitted more than five hundred signatures, negotiated with the utility companies, and succeeded in restoring power and water to the community. In 2006, Nguyen led efforts to close the Chef Menteur landfill. Located only 1.2 miles away from Village de l'Est, the landfill would have housed 6.5 million cubic yards of potentially hazardous waste in an unprotected dump site. Through partnerships with the National Coalition for Asian Pacific American Community Development (National CAPACD), Asian Law Caucus, Louisiana Environmental Action Network, the Sierra Club, and local environmental attorney Joel Waltzer, Nguyen organized residents of Village de l'Est to educate policy makers at the local, state, and national levels. These partnerships resulted in the formation of the Coalition for a Strong New Orleans, a multiracial coalition comprised of neighborhoods throughout the city.

The landfill campaign was organized through a multigenerational effort. Typically, it is common for Vietnamese elders to lead. However, the landfill campaign provided a unique opportunity for the Vietnamese youth to lead through use of social networking. In May 2006, the Vietnamese American Young Leaders Association (VAYLA), a youth organization, emerged out of this multigenerational response to the landfill expansion. On July 14, 2006, Mayor Ray Nagin signed an order to shut down the landfill.

Working with the National Association of Vietnamese American Service Agencies, Nguyen helped to establish the Mary Queen of Vietnam Community Development Corporation (MQVN). MQVN initially played a lead role in providing emergency relief assistance and organizing Vietnamese residents to take an active role in rebuilding the Village de l'Est area. With technical assistance from National CAPACD and other organizations, MQVN worked to ensure long-term housing and home ownership. It implemented the Village de l'Est community recovery plan to develop an eighty-four-unit senior housing complex, a community health center, a business revitalization zone, an urban farm, and a charter school. Today, MQVN aims to foster quality community development, resilience, and celebration of cultures. It works with a range of partners on a wide array of issues including health care, environmental and agricultural concerns, education, housing, social services, economic development, and culture and the arts. The community development corporation's major accomplishments include emergency relief assistance to more than three thousand Vietnamese American residents, the development of a trailer site encompassing 199 homes, and culturally competent case management services to more than 1,200 community members. MQVN has recently completed its $1.8 million New Orleans East Community Health Center, which received its Federally Qualified Health Center designation this year. They also completed their three-acre farm site for the VEGGI Farmer's Cooperative, a farmer-run cooperative that grows local produce utilizing natural and organic practices to promote healthy eating, access to healthy foods, and family economic security.

The story of Village de l'Est has been chronicled extensively by journalists and researchers, including the award-winning PBS film *A Village Called Versailles* (PBS, 2009) and health studies that found rates of posttraumatic stress disorder may be lower within that community. Two points stand out as noteworthy lessons. The first is the importance of community social capital in developing the community resilience to prepare for, cope with, and recover from disasters. The Village de l'Est community enjoyed tight-knit leadership structures, social networks and organization, and cultural ties that contributed to its resilience and adaptive capacity. The community possessed social and cultural capital based on its members' lived experience, including a historical memory rooted in its refugee experience of the 1970s. The existence of a strong faith community added further social support and a strong leadership structure. The importance of social capital and community resilience in disaster response is highlighted by Eric Kleinberg in his study of the 1995 Chicago heat wave, which resulted in nearly five hundred deaths. He found fear of crime, lack of access to healthful facilities, and social isolation in many poor communities in the Chicago Southside where high death rates prevailed. In contrast, communities of similar demographics, such as Little Village in Chicago's West Side, a predominantly Latino community with strong social and family networks, suffered very few deaths (Kleinberg, 2002). Simply put, people in Village de l'Est and Little Village knew and looked out for each other during times of crisis.

The second lesson, related to the first, pertains to how the community's vision for its future built on the same neighborhood assets enabled it to recover so effectively. Gardening and fishing are two important parts of the local culture, health, and economy. MQVN explored aquaponics[1] as a sustainable agriculture and aquaculture alternative that can provide community members the opportunity to combine gardening with household fish farming. Aquaponics technology offered an opportunity for the community to transition toward safer, more environmentally and economically sustainable seafood production, and may be a viable alternative to fishing wild stocks. Aquaponics technology offered a vision for a long-term, profitable, sustainable, and green-job-creating industry with significant environmental benefits (Mary Queen of Vietnam Community Development Corporation, 2015).

Today, MQVN has successfully implemented a pilot aquaponics project in which community growers were trained in the science of aquaponics to develop functional backyard systems. However, the aquaponics startup costs are too high for the low-income population of Village de l'Est. Instead, the growers decided to focus their efforts on a land-based vegetable production for some of New Orleans's finest chefs. The growers supply their vegetables to more than twenty of New Orleans's finest restaurants and two local markets in the New Orleans metropolitan area.

California's Landmark Senate Bill 535

A landmark event in the history of climate justice took place in September 2012 when Governor Jerry Brown signed California's SB 535 into law. SB 535, sponsored by Senator Kevin De Leon, mandated that at least 25 percent of the state's Greenhouse Gas Reduction Fund investments must go to projects that benefit disadvantaged communities, with a minimum of 10 percent of the fund proceeds going to projects located within those communities. During the first year of the fund's operation, SB 535's mandate resulted in $272 million for such projects.

Before I highlight the role of AAPI leadership in the conceptualization, passage, and implementation of SB 535, I must emphasize in the strongest terms that this historic development was the result of community-driven multicultural leadership. In a comprehensive analysis of the history of SB 535 in the *Harvard Civil Rights-Civil Liberties Law Review*, Vien Truong highlighted the role of Shankar Prasad (Truong, 2014). Prasad has often been referred to as the "Father of SB 535." A medical doctor born in India, Prasad has worked throughout his career to utilize science in order to influence public policies in ways that benefit communities most impacted by pollution in the state. As Deputy Secretary for Science and Environmental Justice at the California Environmental Protection Agency (CalEPA), Prasad led the agency in improving the role of science in its decision-making processes, particularly for the most vulnerable communities. He is well known for his strategic thinking and recommendations that have long-term implications in the context of science, policy, and resources. For example, his work resulted in the adoption of environmental justice policies by the California Air Resources Board, initiation of an air pollution toxics research program by the South Coast Air Quality Management District, and the development of "cumulative impacts" as a viable policy construct for addressing vulnerable areas affected by multiple pollution sources and social factors (Breathe California Golden Gate Public Health Partnership, 2011).

Prasad recognized the need for follow-up legislation to realize the promises of Assembly Bill (AB) 32, or the Global Warming Solutions Act, to disadvantaged and environmentally overburdened communities when he worked at CalEPA. He articulated many times that in order to make progress and achieve environmental justice, long-term commitment of a sizeable amount of resources is necessary. Prasad also recognized that carving out from existing resources in the annual budget process was an uphill battle. However, the new large-scale revenue source that would be generated by the cap-and-trade mechanism within AB 32 would be a good source to allocate for the low-income communities that have higher pollution burdens and are more vulnerable to the impacts of climate change. He left CalEPA and joined the Coalition for Clean Air as an Executive Fellow, where he led the efforts for four years to pass a law requiring the intentions of AB 32 to be realized.

Under the banner of the Coalition for Clean Air, Prasad proceeded to organize an alliance to cosponsor the legislation. The initial cosponsoring organizations representing communities throughout California included the Center on Race, Poverty and the Environment, which was subsequently substituted by the California Environmental Justice Alliance; the Ella Baker Center for Human Rights; the Greenlining Institute; the California National Association for the Advancement of Colored People; and the Natural Resources Defense Council. This alliance represented communities of color, environmental justice organizations, civil rights organizations, small and minority-owned businesses, and mainstream environmental organizations.

The SB 535 coalition continues to organize to ensure that SB 535 funds will truly benefit disadvantaged communities affected most by pollution. The Asian Pacific Environmental Network (APEN) leads efforts to organize communities to ensure transformative climate investments that integrate frontline communities into solutions. In "Building a Twenty-First-Century Environmental Movement That Wins," Roger Kim and Martha Matsuoka described how APEN-identified AAPI communities are a critical piece for winning needed progressive policy change in California and how they can be a strong force on climate and clean energy issues. They also point to "a growing landscape of climate activism where community-based groups, organizing in low-income communities and communities of color," had strung together a series of victories that resulted in significant decreases in greenhouse gases and demonstrated a path to a sustainable future." APEN's strategy promotes a "just transition" for highly polluted low-income communities whereby resources are leveraged for carbon pollution reduction projects like local clean energy, clean freight, affordable housing at transit hubs, transit operations, and urban forestry projects (Kim and Matsuoka, 2013, p. 153). The immediate benefits and future promise of APEN's strategy describing funding allocation from SB 535's first year of implementation is illustrated in Figure 2.

Figure 2. Greenhouse Gas Reduction Fund for SB 535 Fiscal Year
2014–15: $272 Million

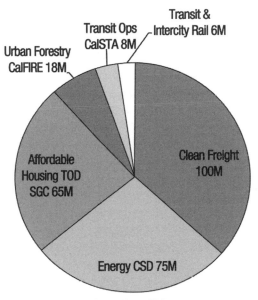

Source: Taruc, 2015

In my blog written for the Environmental Protection Agency's
(EPA's) "EJ in Action" series on the occasion of the twentieth anniversary of President William Clinton's signing of the environmental justice
executive order in 1994, I called SB 535 a harbinger of the future (Lee,
2014). It has implications for climate policy, state innovation, sustainable
development, community revitalization, equitable development, and
environmental justice. It is an example of how states can foster coben-
efits of greenhouse gas reduction for environmentally and economically
distressed communities. This experience may be particularly instructive
as states look to implement the historic Clean Power Plan regulations
recently promulgated by the EPA. SB 535 uses CalEnviroScreen—a sci-
ence-based cumulative impacts screening and mapping tool that takes
into consideration pollution, environmental, health, and socioeconomic
factors—to identify disadvantaged communities. For the first time ever,
environmental factors have been a significant part of determining what
constitutes a "disadvantaged" community. And, perhaps most important, SB 535 provides lessons on the significance of an empowered community voice for transformative environmental decision making.

The Fight for the Future Is Now

Multicultural leadership and multigenerational leadership are hallmarks of successful organizing efforts and were important features of both the Village de l'Est and SB 535 stories, as well as future efforts to meet the pressing issues caused by climate change in the Pacific Islands and other impending environmental challenges. The Village de l'Est story speaks to how AAPIs exerted leadership within and on behalf of their own communities in order to address local issues and leveraged this social capital to achieve common goals for many population groups throughout the city and the nation. It highlights the importance of understanding and building on the cultural assets of communities, particularly immigrant communities and the adaptive capacities derived from unique historical experience. The SB 535 story speaks to the leadership role of AAPIs in a multicultural coalition that functions at many scales, from individual community-level organizing to statewide advocacy, and involving diverse demographic communities, interest groups, and institutions of power. Many AAPIs now hold positions of influence in organizations that affect the environment and can do much to promote the voice of AAPIs on these issues. To name a few, they include David Fukuzawa, Managing Director of Kresge Foundation's Health Programs; Don Chen, Director of Ford Foundation's Metropolitan Opportunity; Vien Truong, National Director of Green for All; Rhea Suh, President of Natural Resources Defense Council; Mathy Stanislaus, Assistant Administrator of the EPA Office of Solid Wastes and Emergency Response; and Grant Nakayama, a leading private-sector environmental attorney and former assistant administrator of the EPA Office of Enforcement and Compliance Assurance.

Youth are a bridge to the future. Both the Village de l'Est and SB 535 stories involve youth in significant ways. VAYLA continues to thrive today as a progressive multiracial community-based organization in New Orleans that empowers youth and families through supportive services and organizing for cultural enrichment and positive social change. As described earlier in this article, young community leaders founded VAYLA in 2006 as a means to reach out to the larger community to create a voice and organize to address the needs in the local community. VAYLA is composed of young leaders, high school and college students that want to engage and empower others educationally, mentally, physically, and spiritually. Today it is committed to youth development, community empowerment, higher education, and cultural awareness (Vietnamese American Young Leaders Association, 2015). Similarly, APEN is nurturing partnerships with AAPI youth organizations like Asian Pacific Islander Youth Promoting Advocacy and East Bay Asian Youth Center to train and empower youth leaders to register voters and build cultures of civic engagement in their communities. APEN combines electoral advocacy with local organizing in the Richmond and Oakland communities of California (Asian Pacific Environmental Network, 2015).

In closing, the most inspiring thing about the leadership illustrated by the two case studies provided in this article is how they are incredibly forward looking. In addressing the crisis and challenges of today, they have carved a pathway to the future. Nowhere are these leadership lessons more important than efforts to address climate change issues in the Pacific Islands. They are fitting examples of why President Clinton said in a *Time* magazine cover article that he was optimistic about the future. Among other things, he cited his participation in a global-sustainability conference in Manaus, Brazil, at the edge of the rain forest. Represented were utilities and oil companies, native Brazilian tribes, small businesses, and environmental groups, as well as the Green Party candidate for president. The delegates sat around small tables, speaking to one another with great respect, believing that if they worked together, they could find an answer. They all understood that if this were a simple issue, someone would have already solved the problem. President Clinton's conclusion, the fight for the future is now, should resonate with all who care about the prospects for addressing the challenges of the environment for 2040, all of which will impact AAPIs in more and more profound ways (Clinton, 2012).

Acknowledgments

The author would like to express his great appreciation for Piyachat Terrell for her assistance in preparing this article.

Notes

1. *Aquaponics* refers to a system that combines conventional aquaculture (raising aquatic animals such as snails, fish, crayfish, or prawns in tanks) with hydroponics (cultivating plants in water) in a symbiotic environment.

References

Asian Pacific Environmental Network. 2015. "Civic Engagement." http://apen4ej.org/what-we-do/civic-engagement/ (accessed October 1, 2015).
Breathe California Golden Gate Public Health Partnership. 2011. "Breathe California Clean Air Award." YouTube. https://www.youtube.com/

watch?v=6uJ1gh5VP5Y (accessed October 1, 2015).

Clinton, William. 2012. "The Case for Optimism: From Technology to Equality, Five Ways the World Is Getting Better All the Time." *Time*, 1 October. http://content.time.com/time/magazine/article/0,9171,2125031-5,00.html (accessed September 23, 2015).

Cotter, Kevin. 2015. "Summary of Laudato Si, Pope Francis' Encyclical on the Environment." Focus. http://www.focus.org/blog/posts/summary-of-laudato-si-pope-francis-encyclical-environment-quotes.html (accessed September 15, 2015).

Hale, Christopher. 2015. "The 5 Most Important Points of Pope Francis' Encyclical." *Time*, 18 June. http://time.com/3925520/pope-francis-climate-change-encyclical/ (accessed September 15, 2015).

Harvey, Chelsea. 2015. "The Most Radical Part of Pope Francis' Message Isn't about Climate Change." *Washington Post*, 17 June. http://www.washingtonpost.com/news/energy-environment/wp/2015/06/17/the-most-radical-part-of-pope-franciss-message-isnt-about-climate-change/ (accessed September 20, 2015).

International Displacement Monitoring Center. 2014. *Global Estimates 2014: People Displaced by Disaster*. http://www.internal-displacement.org/assets/publications/2014/201409-global-estimates2.pdf (accessed September 21, 2015).

Kim, Roger, and Martha Matsuoka. 2013. "Building a Twenty-First-Century Environmental Movement That Wins: Twenty Years of Environmental Justice Organizing by the Asian Pacific Environmental Network." *AAPI Nexus Journal* 11(1–2): 139–58.

Kleinberg, Eric. 2002. *Heat Wave: A Social Autopsy of Disaster in Chicago*. Chicago: University of Chicago Press.

Lee, Charles. 2014. "Evolving Visions of Environmental Justice: Reflections of an EJ Pioneer on EO 12898 after Twenty Years." EJ in Action Blog, US Environmental Protection Agency, 11 February. https://blog.epa.gov/blog/2014/02/evolving-visions-of-ej/ (accessed September 22, 2015).

Leong, Karen J., Airriess, Christopher A., Li, Wei, Chia-Chen Chen, Angela, and Verna M. Keith. 2007. "Resilient History and the Rebuilding of a Community: The Vietnamese American Community in New Orleans East." *Journal of American History* 94: 770–9. http://archive.oah.org/special-issues/katrina/Leong.html (accessed September 22, 2015).

Mary Queen of Vietnam Community Development Corporation. 2015. http://www.mqvncdc.org/ (accessed September 23, 2015).

Pacific Islands Regional Climate Assessment. 2015. "What Is the PIRCA?" http://www.pacificrisa.org/projects/pirca/ (accessed September 21, 2015).

PBS, Independent Lens. 2009. "A Village Called Versailles." http://www.pbs.org/independentlens/village-called-versailles/ (accessed September 23, 2015).

Pope Francis. 2015. *Laudato Si*. Papal Encyclical Letter on the Environment, 24 May. http://w2.vatican.va/content/francesco/en/encyclicals/documents/

papa-francesco_20150524_enciclica-laudato-si.html (accessed March 8, 2016).

Sze, Julie, Ong, Paul, and Charles Lee. 2013. "Asian American and Pacific Islander Environmentalism: Expansions, Connections, and Social Change." *AAPI Nexus Journal* 11(1–2): 83–90.

Taruc, Mari Rose. 2015. "SB 535 Coalition: Engaging EJ Communities for Transformative Climate Investments." Presentation to National Environmental Justice Conference and Training Workshop. Washington, DC, 13 May.

Truong, Vien. 2014. "Addressing Pollution and Poverty: California's SB 535 Greenhouse Gas Reduction Fund." *Harvard Civil Rights-Civil Liberties Law Review* 49: 496–528. http://harvardcrcl.org/wp-content/uploads/2011/09/493_Truong.pdf (accessed September 23, 2015).

Vietnamese American Young Leaders Association. 2015. "VAYLA New Orleans." http://vayla-no.org/ (accessed October 2, 2015).

CHARLES LEE is widely recognized as a true pioneer in the arena of environmental justice. He was the principal author of the landmark report "Toxic Wastes and Race in the United States," the first national study on the demographics of hazardous waste sites. He helped to spearhead the emergence of a national environmental justice movement and federal action including the First National People of Color Environmental Leadership Summit, Executive Order 12898, and the EPA's Office of Environmental Justice. He is currently the Deputy Associate Assistant Administrator for Environmental Justice at the U.S. EPA. The attribution to EPA is for identification purposes only, and the views expressed in the article are those of the author only and do not reflect the agency's policy.

aapi nexus Vol. 14, No. 1 (Spring 2016): 144-161

Practitioner Essay

Reimagining Immigration for a New Generation

Erin Oshiro

Abstract

Do Asian Americans and Pacific Islanders (AAPIs) have a stake in the immigration reform discussion? What types of immigration laws and policies would best serve our community's diverse interests? This article first looks at how AAPIs continue to be impacted by federal immigration laws. Second, it identifies specific immigration policies that need reform and suggests some potential creative policy solutions. Finally, it offers ideas for how—and why—AAPIs can continue to engage in the fight for immigration reform.

Immigration is the most controversial, yet least understood issue in America.

Jose Antonio Vargas, Filipino American journalist and immigrant (Kandil, 2014)

Introduction

While the Asian American and Pacific Islander (AAPI) community continues to grow and welcome many new immigrants, our community has also called America our home for decades.[1] Some AAPI communities have long and deep ties to this country. But, as a collective, AAPIs are also—in both reality *and* public perception—newcomers and foreigners, sometimes exotic but often suspicious. Much of this has to do with America's immigration laws and policies and how they uniquely impact the AAPI experience.

In recent years, outdated and restrictive federal immigration laws have resulted in an untenable situation that does not serve our national, community, or economic interests. Arbitrary numerical limits on green cards keep families separated for decades and prevent businesses from accessing critical employees in a timely manner. Individuals, the majority of whom are Asian nationals, admitted as temporary workers or students find it difficult to transition to permanent resident status. Consequently, restrictions on legal immigration contribute to significant growth in the undocumented immigrant population as individuals continue to come to the United States seeking better opportunities for themselves and their loved ones—papers in hand or not. At the same time, our immigration enforcement system undermines our principles of fairness and due process. While our immigration system is complex, the Asian American immigration experience both informs and contributes to a holistic approach to reform.

Snapshot: AAPIs and Immigration Today

Immigration touches both Asian American and Pacific Islander communities, although sometimes in unique ways, because both have sizable immigrant populations.[2] A discussion on the future of immigration policy in America and its implications for AAPIs should be grounded in our historical and current reality. The history of racist immigration laws and policies specifically directed at Asian nationals is well documented (Hing, 2004; Takaki, 1998), although still not widely known outside the AAPI communities. From 1875 until the early 1950s, Asian immigration was essentially barred. For those Asians who did find their way to the United States, the Supreme Court ruled in *Ozawa v. U.S.* (1922) and *U.S. v. Thind* (1923), respectively, that Asians were not free white people and could be denied naturalized citizenship. Not until the Immigration and Nationality Act of 1952 and amendments in 1965 were race-based restrictions on immigration and naturalization eliminated (Hart-Celler Act, 1965; McCarran-Walter Act, 1952; U.S. Department of State, Office of the Historian). Accordingly, it was not until after 1965 that Asian nationals were able to immigrate to the United States in large numbers and the Asian American community began to grow significantly.

The overwhelming majority of Asian Americans today are immigrants or the children of immigrants, which means that immigration policies continue to significantly impact our community. According to the 2010 Census, there are more than seventeen million Asian Americans in the United States and approximately 60 percent of them are foreign-born—the highest proportion of any racial group (Asian American Center for Advancing Justice, 2011, 3).[3] Many Asian American immigrants are fairly recent newcomers as nearly one in three of the 9.2 million Asian American immigrants came to the United States between 2000 and 2009 (ibid., 17). For more than a decade now, the majority of immigrants to the

United States are from Asian countries (U.S. Department of State, Bureau of Consular Affairs, 2000–14).[4] In 2014 alone, more than one million Asian nationals arrived in the United States—the vast majority arriving with temporary worker or student visas (U.S. Department of State, Bureau of Consular Affairs, 2014a), but many also arrived as refugees and individuals seeking asylum.

Many Asian immigrants came and still come to the United States as refugees due to volatile conditions, war, or strife in their countries of origin. Between 1975 and 2006, the United States admitted 1,306,355 East Asians as refugees to the United States, more than half of the total 2,671,012 refugee population (U.S. Department of State, 2006). Asian refugees increased in recent years and now many Burmese and Bhutanese nationals come to the United States as refugees. For example, in 2011, more than half of new refugees arriving in the United States are from Burma and Bhutan combined (Martin and Yankay, 2013).

As of 2012, approximately 1.3 million Asian American immigrants are undocumented (Baker and Rytina, 2012, 4). Individuals from China, the Philippines, India, Korea, and Vietnam, respectively, comprise the largest number of undocumented Asian immigrants. In addition, due to outdated immigration laws that created years-long backlogs, more than 1.8 million Asian nationals are waiting for visas to reunite with a family member or for permanent employment visas (U.S. Department of State, 2014). Compared to the number of Asian Americans in the United States, Asian nationals represent a disproportionate number of individuals waiting in the visa backlogs (Asian American Center for Advancing Justice, 2011, 19).[5] Further, the overwhelming majority of temporary workers (especially individuals in the United States on "H-1b" visas) and foreign students are now from Asia (U.S. Department of State, Bureau of Consular Affairs, 2014b).[6]

Immigration law also shapes Pacific Islander communities' demographics and experiences. While Native Hawaiians born in the United States, as well as individuals born in Guam and the Commonwealth of the Northern Mariana Islands, are automatically citizens, other Pacific Islander communities are increasingly immigrating to the United States. Like Asian Americans, immigration from the Pacific Islands increased dramatically after 1965. For example, immigration to the United States from Oceania tripled between the 1960s and 1970s (Ong, Ong, and Ong, 2016, 5).[7] By 2000, nearly one in five Pacific Islanders were foreign-born and nearly three-quarters entered since 1980 (ibid.).[8] Among the diverse Pacific Islander community, Fijian, Marshallese Americans, and Palauan Americans are more likely to be foreign-born (Empowering Pacific Islander Communities and Asian Americans Advancing Justice, 2014, 22).

Pacific Islanders who are noncitizens come to the United States with different types of immigration statuses depending on their country of origin. For example, people from American Samoa are "U.S. nationals," which means they can live and work legally in the United States, serve in the military, and qualify for most federal benefits. But U.S. nationals cannot vote in the states unless they become naturalized citizens (ibid., 21). Some other Pacific Islanders are able to work and live in the United States under the Compact of Free Association (COFA), but they are technically considered "nonimmigrants" for purposes of federal immigration laws (ibid.). COFA migrants are eligible to serve in the U.S. military but they are ineligible for most federal benefits. Finally, many Pacific Islanders come from countries with no special relationship with the United States, and they must use the same channels for legal entry and naturalization as any other foreign national. The different immigration statuses among Pacific Islanders mean they may have unique needs and challenges that should be addressed by improved policies beyond just immigration. For example, allowing COFA migrants to access federal benefits, including health care, does not need to be characterized as an immigration matter. Further, future policy changes should acknowledge the special and complex relationships that many Pacific Islander nations have with our country.

We cannot predict future immigration trends with exact certainty but the U.S. Census Bureau forecasts that while the number of AAPI immigrants will grow between now and 2040, the proportion of AAPIs who are immigrants will decrease (Brown, 2015; Ong et al., 2015). For Asian Americans, the percentage of foreign-born and native-born will reach numerical parity (Ong et al., 2015) and for Pacific Islanders the foreign-born will decrease from 20 percent in 2015 to 17 percent in 2040 (ibid., 5–6). This will represent something of a return to our community's pre-1965 demographics when, due to exclusionary immigration laws, there were more native-born AAPIs than foreign-born. As the proportion of AAPI immigrants decreases, how will our community's positions on immigration policy change? Outside our community, will some non-AAPIs continue to view Asian Americans as the "perpetual foreigner," or will our community finally achieve recognition as full Americans—and what would that mean?

Reimagining Immigration in America

At this moment—fifty years after our modern immigration system was created, twenty years after harsh enforcement laws were put in place, and after a decade of failed attempts to reform our immigration laws—we take the opportunity to step back and reimagine what "immigration reform" could mean. If we could completely reinvent our immigration laws, what would we put in place? We do not have space in this article to discuss detailed legislative proposals. But we do present several broad principles that we propose should underlie our future immigration system.

Reexamining Immigration's Purpose

As a starting point, we suggest that America needs to clarify the purpose of our immigration policy. Without a purpose or objective, we foresee a continuing struggle between people's expectations and the federal government's policies and practices. For example, the Immigration and Nationality Act of 1965 prioritized family reunification, but our system of numerically limited family-based visas now results in families being separated for many years. Similarly, laws prohibiting businesses from hiring or employing undocumented workers did not lead to a smaller undocumented population, rather, it forced vulnerable workers without papers into the underground economy. Our humanitarian-based policies for refugees and asylees may no longer meet the changing needs of displaced populations and human rights norms. A fundamental reexamination of the purpose of our immigration policy is necessary to achieve a functioning immigration system that serves America's interests long into the future.

Our Legal Immigration System Needs More Flexibility

A lesson from our current system is that our immigration regime should be more dynamic and responsive to changing conditions, including economic ups and downs, evolving notions of family, and global factors such as political instability and climate change that will force people to migrate. Presently, America's legal immigration is mostly governed by arbitrary and outdated numerical caps that limit the number of family members and workers (permanent and temporary) who can come to the United States each year from each country. For nearly two decades, demand for visas has far outstripped the number of available visas, which is why there are now years-long backlogs for more than four million family members and workers (U.S. Department of State, 2014). The backlogs disproportionately impact certain countries, including several Asian countries, because the numerical limitations do not account for population differences among sending countries, the relative visa demand in some countries versus others, and/or any historical or significant ties between the United States and specific countries (i.e., a land border with Mexico or former colonial relationship with the Philippines). The backlogs represent millions of families putting their lives on hold while they wait for a loved one living abroad, who may miss important life events such as weddings, graduations, and even deaths. Similarly, the lack of immediate visas means employers cannot quickly hire workers for critical jobs. Numerical limits also prevent many Asian temporary workers and students from remaining in the United States and transitioning to a permanent immigrant status (National Foundation for American Policy, 2009; Ruiz, 2014).

America needs an immigration system that balances predictability with flexibility. For example, the United States currently issues sixty-five thousand temporary "H-1b" visas each year to certain skilled workers (Immigration and Nationality Act, 1965, § 214(g)(1)(A)(vii)).[9] What if our businesses need more than sixty-five thousand such workers in a given year? Our system lacks the ability to adapt timely to changing market conditions. Immigration law's definition of *family* is similarly limiting. It was not until after the 2013 Supreme Court decision in *U.S. v. Windsor* that same-sex married couples were recognized for immigration purposes. Should the federal government be in the business of determining which family relationships are most important to citizens and legal permanents, or should private individuals have the ability to determine that for themselves? We need to embed mechanisms in our immigration system that allow for flexibility and adaptation. We also need to break out of our current paradigm of a numerically driven country-based immigration system. Our decisions about who we welcome should not be based solely on numerical limits dictating that only X number of family members can come or that businesses only need Y number of immigrant workers. For example, we could consider establishing numerical minimums for certain types of visas and creating specific criteria for when the numerical limits could be increased (or even lowered), or a commission could be empowered to authorize additional visas in a given year if certain circumstances exist. Or we could permit individual petitioners to demonstrate compelling circumstances why they should be exempt from a numerical limit (e.g., specific health needs, death of a family member in the United States, starting a family business, or another unique business need). The law could also be more fluid in terms of which family members are eligible for visas. Our current system is rigid in terms of which family members can obtain visas and it privileges certain family relationships over others. But what if a U.S. citizen's only surviving relative is her brother—should she have to wait a decade or more to be reunited? Our laws should be more reflective of the diverse family situations that exist today. The current system also unnecessarily pits different classes of immigrants (from different countries) against one another because of rigid definitions. Workers are family members and family members are workers—the distinctions in their visas are arbitrary.

"One-Size-Fits-All" Policies May Not Work

We should be wary of one-size-fits-all policies. The current needs of AAPI immigrants are not always the same as the needs of other immigrant communities. To be sure, all Americans have an interest in creating a functioning immigration system. But specific policy solutions do not necessarily benefit all immigrants equally. The Deferred Action for Childhood Arrivals (DACA) program is a recent example.

Launched in 2012, DACA is an important form of administrative relief that provides temporary protection from deportation and grants work authorization to certain undocumented young people. AAPI leaders were at the forefront of the activism that resulted in DACA. Unfortunately, three years later, relatively few eligible AAPIs have applied for the program (Batalova, Hooker, and Capps, 2014, 13). There are many reasons why AAPI application rates are lower compared to other communities, but one reason is that AAPIs are warier of DACA's temporary nature. It seems that more AAPIs would prefer to hold out for a permanent solution to their unauthorized status, meaning that a program that thousands of Latinos have applied for has not had the same impact in AAPI communities. It also points to the fact that like any constituency, AAPIs must evaluate immigration proposals to determine who will benefit and who will, potentially, be harmed. No national policy will ever be perfect. But AAPIs cannot relinquish their growing power and just assume that an immigration policy beneficial to our interests and values will magically arrive.

Much attention is paid to immigration as an economic driver—and it certainly is. Research amply demonstrates that, overall, immigration is good for our national economy. Immigrants add to our economy as workers, business owners (who create jobs for other Americans), taxpayers, and consumers. For example, immigrants are more likely to start businesses than native-born Americans (Stengler and Wiens, 2015).[10] Americans often hear about the immigrants who transformed Silicon Valley, including the founders of Google, Yahoo, or Intel, or that a significant number of Fortune 500 companies were started by immigrants or their children (Partnership for a New American Economy, 2011, 6). But research and everyday life shows that small local immigrant-owned businesses are just as important to our economic growth and vitality. Immigrants own more than a quarter of local businesses, such as gas stations, dry cleaners, nail salons, and restaurants (Kallick et al., 2015, 5). Immigrant business owners and entrepreneurs have helped revitalize many urban neighborhoods and reverse economic declines (ibid.). Asian Americans are almost half of these so-called Main Street immigrant business owners (ibid.). Beyond business owners, immigrant workers are also significant economic contributors. Undocumented immigrants paid more than $11 billion in state and local taxes in 2012 alone (Gardner, Johnson, and Wiehe, 2015, 2). Having more legal immigrants is a plus for the economy; undocumented immigrants who are able to achieve legal status will likely increase their earnings and be able to contribute even more as taxpayers and consumers (Lynch and Oakford, 2013, 4).

Our immigration policies should support the economic vitality of immigrants. For example, in recent years, many leaders have proposed admitting ever-greater numbers of immigrants with science, technology, engineering, and math (STEM) expertise, or making it easier for foreign students educated in the United States in STEM fields to remain here. However, America should be careful of putting in place short-sighted policies that will repeat the same problems. Certainly, individuals in the STEM fields will be important but there is an open debate about the future growth in these areas, as well as a question about whether there is truly a lack of native-born workers with these skills and expertise (Schaub, 2014). Other relevant changes, including America's aging baby boomer generation and greater educational attainment among native-born Americans, mean we will also continue to need individuals with different skills (often considered lower-skilled workers) and immigrants will help fill critical gaps in our workforce (Partnership for a New American Economy, 2013).[11] Experiences in countries like Canada that implemented preferences for high-skilled workers have found that there is often a mismatch between the immigrants admitted and the types of workers needed in the economy, meaning that even high-skilled immigrants end up unemployed or underemployed (Benderly, 2013; Challinor, 2011, 8–9). Also, policies that disproportionately favor individuals with STEM backgrounds or other advanced degrees will likely mean that fewer women will be able to immigrate to the United States because, globally speaking, women often have less educational access and career opportunities that would provide those types of skills or credentials.

The United States needs an immigration policy that will meet our needs over the long term and that likely means ensuring robust immigration opportunities for immigrants—men and women—with a variety of skills and expertise. In an increasingly global and transnational environment where people and industry are more fluid, we should move beyond mere quota systems that look only at numbers and countries of origin. We will likely need a hybrid system that takes into account national origin and diversity, family relationships, skills, education, and other factors, but where admission to the United States is not dictated by only one or two criteria. For example, some individuals advocate for a "points-based" system, similar to Canada's model, that admits immigrants based on specific characteristics set forth in the law (e.g., educational attainment, employment experience, English or French ability, and age). There could be a positive way to integrate some elements of a "points-based" system, but we would need to ensure that we do not create a system in which only the most well-educated or highly skilled English-speaking individuals can immigrate, and we should preserve channels for family- and employment-based immigrants. For example, the Senate's 2013 bipartisan immigration bill added a points system alongside our current visa categories, but analysis of the bill suggested that women and people with less education or "lower skilled" workers would find it very difficult to immigrate using the points system. Also, the points system in the Senate's bill was added at the unnecessary expense of other existing visa categories. We can have a system that looks more holistically at individuals and evaluates the value they will add to America, but we need a thoughtful discussion about the relative weight of various factors. For instance, the adult child of a U.S. citizen who is moving here to help start a family business could very well have the same "value" as a STEM worker. We hope that future reform discussions will have space for creative thinking and dialogue such as this.

We Must Reframe Immigration Enforcement

Respect for human and civil rights must be at the heart of our immigration system. The national mythology is that America is a nation of immigrants. At best, this is an incomplete story. Asian Americans, perhaps most sharply, know that our immigration history and laws tell a story about who is good, who is desirable, and who we do not want at any given time. As our diversity increases and immigrants continue coming here for better opportunities, Americans must think critically about how we view immigrants and how immigration enriches our community and America overall. Policy makers and the media often rely upon an artificial distinction between "good" immigrants who create jobs and have advanced degrees and "bad" immigrants who take jobs from Americans or live on welfare. AAPIs and all Americans must avoid falling into this false trap of viewing immigrants as simply good or bad. We should collectively reject policies that exacerbate these false dichotomies or create further inequality.

To that end, America needs an enforcement regime grounded in fairness, due process, and proportionality.[12] Since 1996, with the passage of the Illegal Immigration Reform and Immigrant Responsibility Act (IIRIRA), immigration enforcement has been marked by record levels of deportations and detention of immigrants, many of whom are long-term residents with deep community ties, as well as militarization of our southern border. Over time, the increased linkage between our criminal and immigration (which is, strictly speaking, civil) systems has been devastating for communities and has reinforced the notion of good versus bad immigrants. Southeast Asian Americans and some Pacific Islander communities are disproportionately affected. Many Southeast Asians came here as refugees and struggled to rebuild their lives in this new country. Traumatized by war and violence in their home countries, they often experienced poverty, linguistic and cultural barriers, a lack of services, and sometimes violence as they adjusted to their new homes (Fordham Law School, 2010). Some Southeast Asian individuals, many of whom were legal permanent residents, ended up with criminal convictions but did not understand the severe immigration consequences that could follow. Data suggests that Southeast Asians are deported due to criminal convictions at a rate three times higher than other immigrants (Transactional Records Access Clearinghouse, 2016). A more humane enforcement system would not automatically impose the harsh consequence of deportation and the attendant separation from family and community on individuals who have completed their criminal sentences and, in many instances, have turned their lives around.

Moving forward, we need to ensure greater due process in our immigration enforcement policies given how great the stakes are for individuals facing deportation from the United States. For example, IIRIRA essentially eliminated the ability of immigration judges to provide deportation relief to individuals with certain criminal convictions. We should restore judicial discretion to provide relief because judges are in the best position to make such determinations based on the equities and negative factors presented in individual cases. Federal law should go even further to provide court-appointed publicly funded attorneys to represent indigent individuals in deportation proceedings. Currently, not even unaccompanied minor children are provided publicly funded legal representation in immigration court. We also need to consider creative and international strategies for ensuring national security, public safety, and rule of law. Do Americans need to partner more with Canada and Mexico to address border-crossers so that we promote safety, human dignity, and the efficient flow of commerce? At a minimum, America should completely decouple our criminal and immigration systems and begin a new conversation on effective enforcement policies.

Reaffirming Commitment to Humanitarian Relief for Immigrants

A third component to our immigration policy should be how the United States addresses humanitarian crises. Beginning with the waves of Southeast Asian refugees in the late 1970s, Asian Americans had and continue to have a strong connection to our refugee and asylum policies. Large numbers of Burmese and Bhutanese now come to the United States as refugees. However, similar to our visa system and our enforcement regime, our humanitarian-based policies also need to be strengthened, if not reimagined. Two recent examples highlight why America must continue to welcome individuals seeking refuge. In the years since 9/11, it has been increasingly difficult for individuals to come to the United States as refugees because of national security concerns (Human Rights First, 2009). In recent months, there have been calls to halt the admission of Syrian refugees despite the unprecedented humanitarian crisis in Syria, some even going so far as to propose a ban on all Muslim immigrants. How legitimate are these concerns, or are they a pretext for racial and/or religious profiling? The United States has struggled to handle an increased rise in women and children fleeing violence in parts of Central America (Human Rights First, 2015). In general, our asylum laws do not protect individuals who are "merely" fleeing dangerous situations but are not being specifically targeted for violence (Immigration and Nationality Act, 1965, § 101(a)(42)(A); Notess, 2014).[13]

Should our laws be updated to reflect our changing norms and beliefs about human rights? For example, there is increasing attention to the impact of climate change on different populations, including Pacific

Islands that will be affected by rising sea levels. What rights would so-called climate refugees have under existing law? Our current policies are generally ill-equipped to handle these new types of crises, and America should consider new approaches for a changing world. We may also want to consider the treatment of unauthorized immigrants as a form of humanitarian relief rather than our current practice of addressing this through enforcement. Viewing unauthorized immigrants as individuals in need of assistance and relief instead of lawbreakers who need to be deported would mean a radical shift in how we handle the issue of undocumented immigrants. As a matter of self-interest but also as global citizens, the AAPI community should be a part of developing forward-looking solutions that enable us to continue welcoming people seeking protection for a multitude of reasons.

AAPIs Can Play a Role in Reinventing Our Immigration System

As we write this article in 2016, we are far from the dynamic, balanced, and compassionate immigration system that we envision. Congress has been unable to pass even minor changes to our immigration laws, and it is anyone's guess when the next opportunity for meaningful reform will come. But what can our community do to build toward a redefined immigration system?

First, our community must continue supporting and elevating the leadership of immigrants, especially young undocumented AAPIs who are at the forefront of the immigration reform movement. In the past decade, an increasing number of undocumented youth became active in local student groups at their college campuses, and came together to organize for federal legislation that could provide them with a pathway to legal status (Quach, 2009). A bill known as the "Dream Act" (Development, Relief and Education for Alien Minors) was introduced in part after U.S. Senator Richard Durbin from Illinois heard the story of a young undocumented Korean American woman. Tam Tran, a stateless undocumented student from Vietnam, later became the first undocumented immigrant to testify in Congress in 2007 (U.S. House of Representatives, 2007). AAPI activists continue to raise the visibility of immigration as an issue important to our community. In 2011, Jose Antonio Vargas, a Pulitzer Prize–winning journalist, "came out" as an undocumented immigrant from the Philippines in the *New York Times* magazine (Vargas, 2011). In 2013, a "dreamer" from South Korea, Ju Hong, interrupted President Obama during a public event to urge the president to halt deportations (Delreal, 2013). These emerging leaders bring fresh ideas and energy to the fight for immigrants' rights (and the broader civil rights movement), and they will play a critical role in achieving the types of reforms we desire. We must continue including these new leaders in policy discussions and decision making because they are immigrants who will be directly impacted by changes in our immigration laws and policies. At the same time, we must create more opportunities for emerging leaders to tell their stories in their own voices, rather than co-opting their lived experiences or treating their stories as mere media hooks. Steps such as these will help ensure new leaders feel supported and empowered.

Second, AAPIs must continue building alliances with other communities seeking not just better immigration policies but also stronger human and civil rights across the board. Our vision of immigration laws is not just about helping immigrants and their families. Rather, it is rooted in a mission to advance civil and human rights for Asian Americans and to build and promote a fair and equitable society for all. Welcoming new Americans and creating a strong immigration system benefits everyone. So, as AAPIs and other immigrants seek to build coalitions to advance immigrants' rights, we should also work with partners to advance other social justice issues, including criminal justice reform, the rights of LGBTQ individuals, educational equity, and environmental justice. Our communities are collectively stronger when we work in true partnership toward common goals.

Third, as a community we should be mindful of our changing demographics and the potential policy implications. As mentioned earlier, the native-born AAPI population will be increasing over time relative to the foreign-born population. Our community is becoming even more diverse as newer ethnic communities grow while other ethnic communities may experience higher rates of marrying out (i.e., marrying non-AAPIs). And the immigration patterns and experiences of each ethnic community may be somewhat different. For example, a well-educated professional arriving from India or China may find it easier to integrate and succeed than a Bhutanese refugee living in poverty. But, both individuals may also be confronted with Americans who are unfamiliar with our community, diversity, and histories. How can AAPIs—native-born and immigrant—overcome outsiders' misperceptions of us as perpetual foreigners: people who keep their heads down and get good grades? We do not know the answers to these and other difficult questions, but we suggest that a strong awareness of our own evolving community will be important. As AAPIs, we have a responsibility to educate ourselves about our own community and to learn how we are changing. We should care about the challenges of poverty and low educational attainment hurting many Southeast Asian and Pacific Islander communities. Similarly, we should be mindful of the fear and trauma many Sikh, Arab, Muslim, and South Asian Americans still experience in the post–September 11 world of profiling, surveillance, and hate crimes. We need more dialogue among and between our different ethnic groups in order to achieve a greater common understanding of what it means to be AAPI in 2040 and beyond. At the same time, we should continue to think about where AAPIs fit in the larger discussions about race in America. What are we bringing to that dialogue, and how can we contribute to a more equitable society? A greater awareness of our own community's diversity, strengths, and challenges will allow us to maximize our growing political power.

Conclusion

Most Americans understand that our immigration system desperately needs change, and this is an excellent opportunity to galvanize the creativity and political will to imagine an entirely new vision of what our immigration system could or should be. We hope that this essay sparks a conversation among Asian Americans, Native Hawaiians, and Pacific Islanders—and our allies—so we can proactively move toward an America that truly welcomes and embraces newcomers.

Notes

1. This article will not specifically address Native Hawaiians, nearly all of whom are native-born and, therefore, U.S. citizens. According to recent data, only 1 percent of Native Hawaiians are foreign-born.
2. This article does not discuss the different historical policy considerations that may have resulted in different treatment of Asian nationals and Pacific Islanders with regard to immigration.
3. Number combines "Asian alone" and "mixed race."
4. For purposes of this article, immigrant means any individual in the United States who is foreign-born living in the United States. We do not mean immigrant as defined by federal law.
5. Asian Americans sponsor more than one-third of all family-based immigrants. Asian nationals represent 86 percent of individuals waiting for a permanent employment-based visa.
6. E.g., nearly 450,000 student visas were issued to Asian nationals in 2014 compared to almost seventy thousand visas for European nationals.
7. This excludes immigration from Australia and New Zealand.
8. Data is Native Hawaiian-inclusive but does not include migration from U.S. territories.

9. An additional twenty thousand H-1b visas may be issued annually for individuals who earned a master's or higher degree from a U.S. institution of higher education. See Immigration and Nationality Act, 1965, § 214(g)(5).

10. E.g., Stengler and Wiens (2015) found that in 2012 "[i]mmigrants were almost twice as likely to start businesses . . . as native-born Americans."

11. Immigrant workers also play a critical role in shoring up the Social Security Trust Fund. See Partnership for New American Economy, 2013.

12. By "enforcement regime," we mean enforcement in the interior of the United States as well as our borders and ports of entry (e.g., airports). Interior enforcement generally refers to the detection, apprehension, detention, and/or removal of an immigrant in a place other than the border or a port of entry.

13. To qualify for asylum, a person must prove she was persecuted or has a well-founded fear of persecution based on her race, religion, nationality, membership in a particular social group, or political opinion. See Immigration and Nationality Act, 1965, § 101(a)(42)(A). It can be difficult for individuals from countries with "weak rule of law and generalized violence" to obtain asylum because it is more difficult to prove a person was targeted for any of the five protected grounds (or a protected ground was the "central reason" for the persecution) and also if the violence is perpetrated by nonstate actors.

References

Asian American Center for Advancing Justice. 2011. "A Community of Contrasts: Asian Americans in the United States." Asian Pacific American Legal Center and Asian American Justice Center. Report.

Baker, Bryan, and Katrina Rytina. U.S. Department of Homeland Security. 2012. *Estimates of the Unauthorized Immigrant Population Residing in the United States: 2012.* Washington, DC: Office of Immigration Statistics. http://www.dhs. gov/sites/default/files/publications/ois_ill_pe_2012_2.pdf (accessed March 4, 2016).

Batalova, Jeanne, Hooker, Sarah, and Randy Capps. 2014. "DACA at the Two-Year Mark: A National and State Profile of Youth Eligible and Applying for Deferred Action." Migration Policy Institute, Report.

Benderly, Beryl Lieff. 2013. "Canada to Scrap Points System for High-Skilled Immigration." *Science Careers*, 26 April.

Brown, Anna. 2015. "U.S. Immigrant Population Projected to Rise, Even as Share Falls among Hispanics, Asians." *Pew Research Center*, 9 March.

Challinor, A. E. 2011. "Canada's Immigration Policy: A Focus on Human Capital." *Migration Policy Institute*, 15 September. http://www.migrationpolicy. org/article/canadas-immigration-policy-focus-human-capital (accessed January 6, 2016).

Delreal, Jose. 2013. "Heckler 'Disappointed' by Obama." *Politico*, 26 November.

Empowering Pacific Islander Communities and Asian Americans Advancing

Justice. 2014. "A Community of Contrasts: Native Hawaiians and Pacific Islanders in the United States." Report.

Fordham Law School, Walter Leitner Human Rights Clinic. 2010. "Removing Refugees: U.S. Deportation Policy and the Cambodian-American Community." http://searac.org/sites/default/files/2010%20Cambodia%20Report_FINAL.pdf (accessed March 4, 2016).

Gardner, Matthew, Johnson, Sebastian, and Meg Wiehe. 2015. "Undocumented Immigrants' State and Local Tax Contributions." *The Institute on Taxation & Economic Policy*, April.

Hart-Celler Act (Immigration and Nationality Act of 1965). HR 2580. 89th Cong., 1st sess. Cong. Rec. 79 Stat. 911 (P.L. 89-236). https://en.wikipedia.org/wiki/Immigration_and_Nationality_Act_of_1965 (accessed March 30, 2016).

Hing, Bill Ong. 2004. *Defining America through Immigration Policy*. Philadelphia: Temple University Press.

Human Rights First. 2015. "U.S. Detention of Families Seeking Asylum: A One Year Update." Report, June.

———. 2009. "Denial and Delay: The Impact of the Immigration Law's 'Terrorism Bars' on Asylum Seekers and Refugees in the United States." Report.

Kallick, David Dyssegaard, Brick, Kate, McCutcheon, Steven, Segal, Susan, Andre, Richard, and Zachary Bleckner. 2015."Bringing Vitality to Main Street: How Immigrant Small Businesses Help Local Economies Grow." Americas Society and Fiscal Policy Institute, Report, January.

Kandil, Kaitlin Yoshiko. 2014. "Jose Antonio Vargas Films for Immigration Reform." *San Jose Inside*, 5 March. http://www.sanjoseinside.com/2014/03/05/jose-antonio-vargas-films-for-immigration-reform/ (accessed January 5, 2016).

Lynch, Robert, and Patrick Oakford. 2013. "The Economic Effects of Granting Legal Status and Citizenship to Undocumented Immigrants." *Center for American Progress*, 20 March.

Martin, Daniel C., and James E. Yankay. U.S. Department of Homeland Security. 2013. *Refugees and Asylees: 2013*. Washington, DC: Office of Immigration Statistics. http://www.dhs.gov/publication/refugees-and-asylees-2013 (accessed March 30, 2016).

McCarran-Walter Act (Immigration and Nationality Act of 1952). HR 5678. 82nd Cong., 2nd sess. Cong. Rec. 182 Stat. 66. P.L. No. 414. https://en.wikipedia.org/wiki/Immigration_and_Nationality_Act_of_1952 (accessed March 30, 2016).

National Foundation for American Policy. 2009. "Employment-Based Green Card Projections Point to Decade-Long Waits." Policy Brief, November.

Notess, Laura. 2014. "Consideration for Hondurans in the American Asylum Process: Relevant Law and Country of Origin Information." Jesuit Conference of the United States. http://jesuits.org/Assets/Publications/File/Hondurans_asylum_report_FINAL.pdf (accessed March 28, 2016).

Ong, Paul, Ong, Elena, and Jonathan Ong. 2016. "The Future of Pacific Islander

America in 2040." *AAPI Nexus Journal: Policy, Practice, and Community* 14(1): 1–13.

Partnership for New American Economy. 2015. "America's Aging Crisis: How Immigration Reform Can Strengthen the U.S. Workforce." http://www.renewoureconomy.org/wp-content/uploads/2015/07/PNAE-Aging-Workforce-2.pdf (accessed December 17, 2015).

———. 2013. "America's Aging Crisis: How Immigration Reform Can Strengthen the Coverage for U.S. Seniors." http://www.renewoureconomy.org/wp-content/uploads/2015/07/PNAE-Aging-Coverage.pdf (accessed January 6, 2016).

———. 2011. "The 'New American' Fortune 500." Report.

Quach, Hoa. 2009. "USA: Blogging Their Dreams of Citizenship." Global Voices Online. http://globalvoicesonline.org/2009/01/23/usa-blogging-their-dreams-of-citizenship/ (accessed March 4, 2016).

Ruiz, Neil G. 2014. "The Geography of Foreign Students in U.S. Higher Education: Origins and Destinations." *Brookings*, 29 August.

Schaub, Hillary. 2014. "The Importance of the Science and Engineering Workforce for Future Growth." *Brookings*, 23 April.

Stengler, Dane, and Jason Wiens. 2015. "The Economic Case for Welcoming Immigrant Entrepreneurs." *Kaufmann Foundation*, 8 September.

Takaki, Ronald. 1998. *Strangers from a Different Shore*. Boston: Little, Brown.

Transactional Records Access Clearinghouse, Syracuse University. 2016. "U.S Deportation Outcomes by Charge: Completed Cases in Immigration Courts." http://trac.syr.edu/phptools/immigration/court_backlog/deport_outcome_charge.php (accessed July 15, 2015).

U.S Department of State. 2014. Annual Report of Immigrant Visa Applicants in the Family-Sponsored and Employment-Based Preferences Registered at the National Visa Center as of November 1, 2014. Washington, DC: Government Printing Office. http://travel.state.gov/content/dam/visas/Statistics/Immigrant-Statistics/WaitingListItem.pdf (accessed October 6, 2015).

———. 2006. Summary of Refugee Admissions for Fiscal Year 2006. Archive. http://2001-2009.state.gov/g/prm/refadm/rls/85970.htm (accessed October 6, 2015).

U.S. Department of State, Bureau of Consular Affairs. 2014a. Report of the Visa Office. https://travel.state.gov/content/visas/en/law-and-policy/statistics/annual-reports/report-of-the-visa-office-2014.html (accessed October 5, 2015).

———. 2014b. FY 2014 Nonimmigrant Visas Issued Summary Table. https://travel.state.gov/content/dam/visas/Statistics/Non-Immigrant-Statistics/NIVDetailTables/FY14NIVDetailTable.pdf (accessed October 6, 2015).

———. 2000–14. "Reports of the Visa Office." http://travel.state.gov/content/visas/english/law-and-policy/statistics.html (2000-2014) (accessed October 5, 2015).

U.S. Department of State, Office of the Historian. n.d. *Milestones: 1945–1952*. https://history.state.gov/milestones/1945-1952/immigration-act (accessed

March 4, 2016).

U.S. House of Representatives. 2007. Committee on the Judiciary. Subcommittee on Immigration, Citizenship, Refugees, Border Security and International Law. *Comprehensive Immigration Reform: The Future of Undocumented Immigrant Students* (testimony of Tam Tran). Hearing.

Vargas, Jose Antonio. 2011. "My Life as an Undocumented Immigrant." *New York Times*, 22 June.

ERIN OSHIRO is the former director of Immigration and Immigrants' Rights at Asian Americans Advancing Justice | AAJC. Oshiro directed advocacy efforts to create more humane and just federal immigration policies and practices. Prior to joining Advancing Justice | AAJC, she was an Equal Justice Works Fellow and worked in private practice in New York. Oshiro earned her bachelor's degree and law degree from the University of California at Los Angeles.

aapi nexus Vol. 14, No. 1 (Spring 2016): 162-178

Practitioners Essay

From Citizens to Elected Representatives:
The Political Trajectory of Asian American Pacific Islanders by 2040

Christine Chen, James S. Lai,
Karthick Ramakrishnan, and Alton Wang

Abstract

The political power of Asian Americans and Pacific Islanders (AAPIs) has increased steadily in the United States. By 2040, one in ten Americans will be AAPI, and the number of Asian Americans registered to vote will have doubled (Ong, Ong, and Ong, 2016). This section examines the growing AAPI electorate and projects a trajectory for AAPI civic engagement and political participation from now until 2040. By looking at trends and projections for citizenship, voter registration, voter turnout, elected officials, and political infrastructure, the authors illustrate that AAPI political empowerment will have even a greater influence on the future of American politics.

Introduction

The political power of Asian Americans and Pacific Islanders (AAPIs) has increased steadily in the United States as the size of the AAPI population has grown. By 2040, one in ten Americans will be AAPI, and the number of Asian Americans registered to vote will have doubled (Ong, Ong, and Ong, 2016). The number of Pacific Islanders is also expected to significantly increase based on projected population growth. However, there are currently no detailed projections of the number of registered Pacific Islanders. This section examines the growth of the AAPI electorate and presents a trajectory for AAPI civic engagement and political participation from now until 2040.

AAPIs have been suggested to be the potential new "sleeping giant" in American politics (Ong, De La Cruz-Viesca, and Nakanishi, 2008). The projections of the AAPI electorate presented here assert this possibility—

that AAPI voters have the very real potential of becoming an increasingly powerful political force, even beyond high-intensity elections. Growth in the AAPI electorate can translate to growth in the number of AAPI elected officials or other governmental positions, giving AAPI communities increased political influence and the ability to shape public policy.

By looking at the trends and projections in AAPI voting population, including citizenship, voter registration, voter turnout, elected officials, and political infrastructure, the authors delve into an analysis of AAPI political power—presenting a future where this power could yield even greater influence over the future of American politics.

Current Trends in AAPI Political Participation

Voting Population and Trends

Political power through the ballot is more complex than the vote—individuals must be citizens, whether through birth or naturalization, then be registered to vote, and finally turn out to vote. The AAPI population is heavily immigrant, and each stage presents its own challenges and barriers that may stymie possibly even more substantial growth in electoral power (Ong and Nakanishi, 1996, Ramakrishnan 2005).

Among immigrants, Asian immigrants have consistently been among the fastest of any group to naturalize. As Table 1 shows, those from North American countries have averaged about ten years, while those from Asian countries have averaged about seven years. Various factors help explain these quicker rates of naturalization among Asian immigrants, including longer distance to homelands, coming from repressive regimes, and individual characteristics such as income and education (Waters and Pineu, 2015). Among Asian immigrant groups, rates of citizenship are highest among Southeast Asian refugee groups (75 percent or higher among adult Hmong, Laotians, and Vietnamese Americans) and are also high among Filipino and Japanese Americans (more than 70 percent). By contrast, citizenship rates are lowest among South Asian populations (50 percent for Sri Lankans, 55 percent for Indians, 56 percent for Bangladeshis, and 67 percent for Pakistanis). These differences are largely attributable to the fact that South Asian immigrants are more recently arrived, on average, than other Asian immigrants, and also have a lower proportion of U.S.-born residents given their more recent arrival and ongoing increases in migration (which stands in sharp contrast to relatively fewer immigrants coming from such countries as Laos, Cambodia, and Vietnam).

Table 1. Median Years to Naturalize by Region of Birth

	2012	2010	2000	1990	1980
Total	7	6	9	8	8
Africa	5	5	7	7	7
Asia	6	5	8	7	7
Europe	7	6	7	10	10
North America	10	10	11	11	11
Oceania	8	7	11	10	8
South America	6	5	10	9	9

Source: Ramakrishnan and Ahmad, 2014

Despite higher rates of naturalization, AAPIs over the past two decades have lagged behind other groups in terms of their voting participation (for a review of this literature, see Lien, 2001; Ramakrishnan, 2005; Wong, 2006), and this pattern continued to hold true in the 2012 presidential election. As indicated in Table 2, voting rates among adult citizens in 2012 were highest among African Americans (66 percent) and non-Hispanic whites (64 percent). Voting among Asian Americans (47 percent) and Pacific Islanders (49 percent) was significantly lower due to multiple factors such as limited English proficiency (LEP), antiimmigrant sentiment, and other systemic barriers.

Table 2. Rates of Citizenship, Voter Registration, and Turnout

	Citizens	Registered	Voted	Voted
	(among adults)	(among adult citizens)	(among registered)	(among adult citizens)
White	98%	73%	87%	64%
Hispanic	66%	59%	82%	48%
African American	95%	73%	91%	66%
Asian	66%	56%	84%	47%
American Indian	99%	64%	80%	51%
NHPI	88%	58%	85%	49%

Source: Ramakrishnan and Ahmad, 2014

Lower citizenship rates are not the only important factor that is holding back the electoral potential of Asian Americans. When breaking down voting into its component categories, we see that the racial gaps are far more significant when it comes to *voter registration*. Compared to non-Hispanic whites and African Americans at 73 percent, the Asian American voter registration rate is 56 percent and the Pacific Islander voter registration rate is 58 percent, respectively, roughly fifteen to seventeen percentage points lower (or on a proportional basis, 23 percent lower).

In contrast, when it comes to *turnout among registered voters*, Asian American turnout is 84 percent and Pacific Islander turnout is 85 percent, only three to seven percentage points lower (or 4 percent to 10 percent lower on a proportional basis) when compared to whites and African Americans.

A reason for these registration and turnout rates could be that many in the AAPI community are LEP, making language access and Section 203 of the Voting Rights Act a critical part of civic and political participation for AAPIs across the country.[1] The "Behind the Numbers" 2012 Post Election Survey by Asian Americans Advancing Justice—AAJC, Asian and Pacific Islander American Vote (APIAVote), and National Asian American Survey found that turnout for LEP AAPIs was nine percentage points lower (75 percent) than those who could speak English proficiently (84 percent). Another reason for these trends could be because of the anti-immigrant and xenophobic rhetoric exhibited by political candidates.[2]

Other barriers to increased engagement are systematic in nature. Currently, Asian Americans at 56 percent and Pacific Islanders at 58 percent have the lowest voter registration rates. Eliminating systemic barriers to democratic participation can potentially increase AAPI political engagement. For example, in Oregon and California (which have sizeable AAPI populations of 243,000 and 6,364,000, respectively) legislation has been passed to institute automatic voter registration. It is predicted that there may be more than twenty thousand new AAPI voters in Oregon, as well as hundreds of thousands of new AAPI voters in California, added to the voter rolls. So while AAPI voters will be registered automatically through these systems, much work will still need to be done to educate and motivate these voters to cast their ballot. These new AAPI voters will likely have lower levels of political interest and political efficacy than AAPIs who actively choose to register to vote.

Although automatic registration is currently limited, online voter registration is increasingly available. According to the National Council of State Legislators, as of January 4, 2016, a total of twenty-nine states plus the District of Columbia offer online registration. Based on U.S. Census surveys, we know that more than 86 percent of Asian American households have access to the Internet (File and Ryan, 2014). Online voter registration systems will supplement the traditional paper-based system. The online systems will allow an individual to complete his or her voter registration form using an Internet site, and have that paperless form submitted electronically to election officials. We anticipate that this could have a positive effect on AAPI political participation.

Same-day registration is currently available in eleven states plus the District of Columbia. This allows any qualified resident of the state to go to the polls or an election official's office on Election Day, register that day, and then vote. Minnesota (where AAPIs account for 3.1 percent of eligible voters) has implemented this practice since 1974, and currently has the highest voter turnout rate in the country. California, Hawaii, and Vermont (where AAPIs are 15 percent, 66 percent, and 1 percent of the total share of eligible voters, respectively) have enacted same-day registration but have not yet implemented it. If implemented, it could affect turnout by increasing the likelihood that AAPI voters will be courted in a culturally and linguistically sensitive manner.

At the national level there is a movement to eliminate barriers to voting by increasing "no excuse" absentee voting. As of 2014, twenty-eight states and the District of Columbia allow "no excuse" absentee voting and twenty-one states require an excuse to vote absentee. Oregon and Washington (where AAPIs are 4.1 percent and 7.8 percent of the total share of eligible voters, respectively) are the only states that employ a vote-by-mail-only system. In California, which has long had permanent and "no excuse" absentee voting, almost 50 percent of voters vote by mail. Those with strict excuse requirements, such as Tennessee (where AAPIs are 1.2 percent of eligible voters), have only 5 percent of voters who vote by mail. For some of these states, an excuse of serving in an election role, student status, working, or jury duty does not qualify as an excuse.

Figure 1. Absentee Voting Can Increase Turnout among Language Minorities

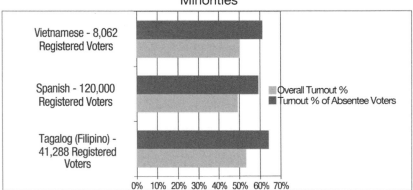

Source: San Diego County Registrar of Voters

As seen with Figure 1, a case study in San Diego County, absentee voting can increase the turnout among language minorities.

Currently, at 47 percent, Asian Americans are the "least likely" to vote, and Pacific Islanders are the third least likely at 49 percent. Efforts to increase naturalization and language access through Section 203 and culturally sensitive and linguistically appropriate outreach and campaigning will likely increase AAPI political engagement and participation. Efforts to address systemic barriers—such as online, as well as in-person, voter registration—must be done in a linguistically and culturally nuanced way, otherwise it could have a net negative effect on AAPI political participation.

AAPI Elected Representation

Another aspect of political participation that extends beyond voting and public opinion is elected representation. AAPI elected representation is an important litmus test for AAPI political power. This issue is and will continue to be a crucial and pivotal centerpiece for AAPI political participation and incorporation in U.S. politics.

Figure 2. Total Number of APAEOs in Key Elected Positions, 1978–2014

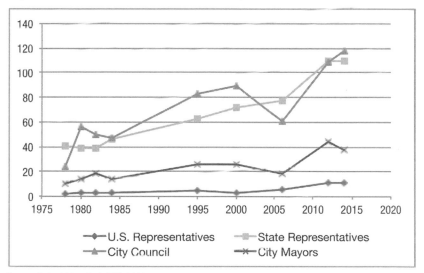

Source: Nakanishi and Lai, 1978–2014

Figure 2 illustrates the steady increase in the total number of Asian Pacific American elected officials (APAEOs) at all levels of government taking shape from 1978 to 2014 corresponding to each edition of the

National Asian Pacific American Political Almanac.[3] Most noticeably these gains have been at the local and state levels with the elected positions of city council and state representatives. Local officials (city mayors and city council members) and state officials (state representatives) have increased the most rapidly during this period compared to the total number of federal representatives. These changes symbolize the gradual political incorporation of AAPIs, which contain the largest foreign-born population in 2014 among all racial groups, into U.S. politics. Despite this growth, AAPIs still lag behind other racial minority groups with large foreign-born populations such as Latina/os. In 2015, the total number of Latina/o state representatives and state senators were 231 and 74, respectively, and the total number of municipal elected officials was 1,800 (National Association of Latino Elected Officials Education Fund, 2015). In comparison, in 2014, the total number of AAPI state representatives and state senators were seventy-three and twenty-five, respectively.

As Figure 2 demonstrates, local politics remains a primary entry way into U.S politics, and this is no different for AAPIs, both young and old, U.S.-born and immigrant. Geographic diversity is also another hallmark of AAPI elected representation. Prior to the 1990s, a majority of APAEOs came from the two states of Hawaii and California. For example, in 1978, among the total 161 APAEOs in the United States, California and Hawaii accounted for seventy-eight (48 percent) and sixty-two (39 percent), respectively. Only eight other states had APAEOs.[4] While California and Hawaii still account for the largest percentage of APAEOs in 2014, a total of thirty-one states were represented among those with APAEOs.

The number of AAPIs serving as presidential political appointees has also continued to increase with every administration since the 1993–2001 Clinton administration. During the 2009–17 Obama administration, at one point the AAPI community had three secretaries of Asian descent serving in the cabinet: Secretary of Commerce Gary Locke, Secretary of Energy Steven Chu, and Secretary of Veterans Affairs Eric Shinseki. In addition, the Obama administration has tripled the number of Asian Pacific American judges on the federal bench, going from eight judges to twenty-four active Article III APA judges since 2008.

AAPI Political Infrastructure

"Political infrastructure" encompasses the community's ability to build a political pipeline, the number of institutional structures, as well as an organization's ability to scale up and build capacity to meet the needs of this ever-growing diverse community. Twenty-five years ago, the AAPI community political infrastructure was far more of a skeleton than it is today. There were only four national Asian American civil rights organizations based in the nation's capital with a combined staff of eight addressing policy issues of importance to the community. AAPIs on Capitol Hill, in the White House, and in federal agencies were just as scarce. Within the last two decades not only has the AAPI community grown, but, along with it, an infrastructure to represent and advocate for themselves. At the same time, continued development and investment in these structures are needed for it to be more effective.

More than twenty years ago, on Capitol Hill, the Congressional Asian Pacific American Staff Association was founded to provide support to those working on Capitol Hill. In 1994, the Congressional Asian Pacific American Caucus (CAPAC) was founded. Today, CAPAC has grown to forty-eight members. Today there are thirteen U.S. members of Congress of Asian and Pacific Islander descent, the largest number in U.S. history. Recently, CAPAC also created the Asian Pacific American Caucus (PAC) to help support AAPI candidates running for federal seats.

In 1996, the National Council of Asian Pacific Americans (NCAPA) was founded. Today there are thirty-five national AAPI organizations that belong to this national coalition of national Asian American, Native Hawaiian, and Pacific Islander organizations. The organization strives for equity and justice by leveraging the diverse strengths of Asian Americans and Native Hawaiians and Pacific Islanders to shape the public discourse and influence public policy. To align with congressional policy making, NCAPA develops a policy blueprint to guide advocacy efforts.

In 1999, President Bill Clinton signed an executive order creating the White House Initiative on Asian Americans and Pacific Islanders (WHIAAPI). Since then it has been renewed and its focus modified based on the priorities of the administration. In 2009, President Obama reauthorized WHIAAPI and the President's Advisory Commission on AAPIs. Over the past six years, the initiative and commission have connected with almost one hundred thousand individuals in numerous states and cities across the country, including the Pacific Islands. More than twenty agencies have developed robust strategic plans that lay out strategies, objectives, and possible outcomes on a range of issues, including promoting data disaggregation and language access; increasing resources to AAPI organizations and communities; and improving diversity in the federal workforce.

More recently, there has also been a rapid growth in the civic infrastructure focused on voter engagement of AAPI communities. In 2014, for example, 317 AAPI-serving organizations participated in National

Voter Registration Day, more than double the number of organizations that participated in 2012. A growing number of community-based organizations are integrating voter registration into their regular activities and programs throughout the year. In doing so, these organizations are amplifying and reinforcing the importance of civic engagement, especially when growing civic participation increases the ability of organizations to advocate for their communities' interests. Today, AAPIs are actively turning out the vote for the 2016 presidential election, as a broad network of AAPI organizations continue their legacy of participating in the APIA Presidential Town Hall.

The growth of AAPI civic participation is due not only to the fact that community organizations are getting more involved, but also because of the growing number of AAPI elected officials and candidates running for office. Every time a leader from the community decides to run for elected office, or seek political appointment, she or he engages her or his network of extended family and friends to get involved.

The growth of AAPI elected officials is supported with the growth of AAPI political infrastructure and AAPI political resources. Over the last quarter of a century, more political PACs and Democratic and Republican clubs and caucuses have been established. The latest edition is the AAPI Victory Fund, the first Super PAC focused on engaging the AAPI electorate. We also see a growing number of staffers of AAPI descent involved with campaigns at all political levels. Since the 1990s, the Democratic National Committee has had an AAPI community desk focused on engagement with the AAPI community. In 2013, the Republican National Committee hired staff and provided assistance in outreach to AAPIs in several states. With this development of a political pipeline, infrastructure, and resources, we now have the ingredients for the AAPI community to increase civic engagement and to ensure that participation in the democratic process truly reflects America's diversity.

Likely Trajectory in AAPI Political Participation In 2040

Likely AAPI Voting Trajectory

For immigrants, U.S. citizenship is a prerequisite for registering to vote and voting. Yet, per the Urban Institute, immigration reform proposals could cut the number of family visas to admit more people based on their job skills. As a result, more high-skilled immigrants will come from India, China, and the Philippines. In the future, we could expect the number of citizens from South Asian countries to increase significantly, as immigrants stay longer in the United States and get settled in various communities. At the same time, their rates of citizenship will not increase as quickly, given expectations of continued new migration from South Asian countries. Finally, we can expect Southeast Asian refugee groups to have even greater rates of citizenship, as the population gets more settled and there are reductions in future waves of immigrants and refugees from these countries. Should there be a war or immigration reform, we might also see an increase in the number of Asians from other nations.

While a large proportion of Asian American voters are immigrants in 2015, the U.S.-born voting population is close to eclipsing the Asian American immigrant vote by 2040. For example, the U.S.-born Asian American population is going to get older, on average, in 2040 when compared to the U.S.-born population today. Based on existing research on voting patterns by age and nativity (Ong, Ong, and Ong, 2016; Ramakrishnan, 2005; Wong et al., 2011), we can surmise that, in the future, this will mean higher rates of voting participation among second-generation Asian Americans (see Figure 3). In addition, the proportion of native-born Asian Americans is projected to increase from about 40 percent in 2010 to 50 percent in 2040 (Ong, Ong, and Ong, 2016).

Figure 3. Asian American Registered Voters by Citizen Status (in thousands)

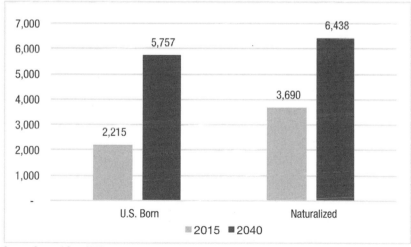

Source: Ong and Ong, 2015

Finally, even though immigration will continue to fuel the growth of Asian Americans in the future, the immigrant population is getting more and more settled over time, spending more years in the United States, and getting older. As the proportion of long-term residents and seniors among Asian Americans continues to grow, we should expect to see an increase in the overall rate of voter registration and voting (see Figure 4). Importantly, however, the sizable and growing share of undocumented Asian immigrants will serve as a future drag on citizenship and voting participation (Rosenblum and Soto 2015)

Figure 4. Asian American Registered Voters Totals by Nativity and Age, 2015 and 2040

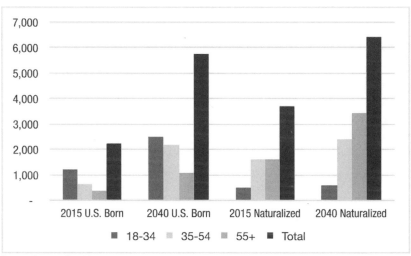

Source: Ong and Ong, 2015

Likely Trajectory in AAPI Elected Officials

Looking forward to 2040, AAPIs will likely become a growing political force as swing voters, active participants in community-based organizations and political clubs, coalition partners, commissioners, and elected officials at the local, state, and national level. Active participation in these organizations can result in the recruitment and mentoring of potential AAPI political candidates (Lai, 2009, 2011; Wong, 2006).

The geographic location of where future APAEOs are likely to be elected will continue to reflect two current trends. First, APAEOs will likely continue to be elected in local, state, and federal districts where Asian Pacific Americans are a minority. In these minority districts, some evidence suggests that Asian Pacific American candidates have a greater chance of winning from these areas than those with large percentages of Asian Pacific Americans (Ong and Lee, 2010). In districts where Asian

Pacific Americans are a minority, they will continue to be important swing voters.

Second, the suburbs, particularly those emerging with a majority or plurality AAPI districts will likely continue to fuel the largest number of future APAEOs and candidates in various city councils and school boards, which allow AAPI voters to vote for AAPI candidates. These cities can be found both in major Asian populated states such as California, Hawaii, and Washington, but also in emerging Asian populated states such as Maryland, Illinois, Virginia, and Texas to city commissions that will allow for political networks to develop.[5] Thus, redistricting of district boundaries will play a central role in maximizing or diluting voting blocs among AAPIs from taking shape (Kwoh and Hui, 1993; Ong and Lee, 2010). Regardless of group population size, successful AAPI candidates at all levels of government will need to build multiethnic, multiracial, and multi-issue political coalitions among diverse voters, contributors, and interest groups, non-AAPI and AAPI alike (Lai, 2011).

Finally, the long-term trajectory of AAPI elected representation must continue to involve both political pipelining and vertical political incorporation. Political pipelining at the local level is the critical stage of local APAEOs appointing well-qualified, potential AAPI candidates to high-profile city commissions to develop political networks and experiences should they choose to run later for open seats on city councils.[6] AAPIs, like all groups, must run for open seats at the local, state, and federal levels. With regard to political incorporation, AAPIs have successfully demonstrated political incorporation in various cities, which resulted in multiple and, in some cases, majority Asian American city councils on the continental United States where AAPIs are making key decisions on policies that effect entire cities with significant AAPI populations (ibid.).

Likely Trajectory in AAPI Political Infrastructure

As we look toward the future, we foresee that existing organizations will increase their resources and capacity to develop effective programs to address growing AAPI political pipeline and advocacy efforts. The sophistication of the AAPI political community will be well developed by 2040.

We have already observed that more organizations are willing to incorporate and explicitly focus on implementing voter registration, education, and get-out-the-vote programs. With each election cycle, AAPIs are becoming more comfortable with campaign work and, in some cases, start implementing more effective tactics such as securing media coverage, door-to-door canvassing, and phone banking. Between the ongoing growth of the AAPI community and by their success stories, the AAPI electorate will likely receive attention from political candidates, fundraisers, and parties. With more of the community being exposed to voter participation, it is also growing the AAPI political pipeline.

Closing the Gap between the Likely and Desired Trajectory

Despite a likely upward trajectory in voting that will proceed faster than the growth rate of the population, we still anticipate gaps in voting among AAPIs, on the one hand, and whites and African Americans, on the other. That is because, even among the groups who are most likely to participate (seniors, college educated, U.S.-born), AAPI voting has lagged significantly behind the national average. Thus, even with the growing share of seniors among AAPIs and the aging of the second-generation population into middle age, we expect that AAPI voting will be lower than the overall voting rate in 2040, although these gaps will likely be smaller than in 2012.

That is why today, organizations like APIAVote are developing strategies to engage voters, including youth and seniors. Voter engagement campaigns utilizing various platforms—from digital and social to direct voter contact—engage AAPIs on several fronts. Youth outreach for APIAVote is centered around working with existing youth networks and tapping into AAPI influencers in an effort to increase the discourse around civic engagement as a whole. Senior outreach will be as nuanced, with today's forty-year-olds being 2040's senior vote base.

Additionally, many in the AAPI community are LEP and may continue to be. Language assistance is critical in ensuring all AAPIs have access to the ballot and be informed voters in the democratic process. Even in areas with high AAPI populations not covered under Section 203, language access initiatives are important undertakings. For example, in Fairfax County, Virginia, community organizers worked with the board of elections to translate materials to Korean, serving the large Korean community in the area. Going into the future the potential growth in language access provisions and initiatives will determine the engagement of AAPIs with the ballot. By 2040, we will see an increase of U.S.-born Asian voters; however, there will still be a need for translated ballots and educational materials because another generation of new immigrants will continue to arrive.

Other factors that could impede AAPI political engagement and participation include antiimmigrant hostility, China bashing, and other anti-Asian sentiments from blogs, presidential candidates, and more. Often statements that promote AAPIs as a perpetual foreigner are made by campaigns as a scare tactic to dampen or suppress AAPI enthusiasm for, and involvement in, the democratic process. But these tactics may no longer work among a newly engaged, and emboldened, AAPI electorate.

Recent polling has shown that the AAPI electorate is not submissive, and it will not tolerate ignorance: 41 percent of AAPIs would change their support of a candidate if that candidate was anti-immigrant (Asian and Pacific Islander American Vote and Asian Americans Advancing Justice—AAJC, 2014). This statistic is a wake-up call, warning candidates that divisive language will not be tolerated or forgiven by the AAPI community. The AAPI electorate is not politically expendable. In fact, AAPIs play a key role as a swing vote in many areas.

Indeed, AAPIs comprise 5 percent or more of the eligible adult voting-age population in seven states, seventy-three counties, and 103 congressional districts (Ramakrishnan and Ahmad, 2014), and AAPI voters are up for grabs in terms of party affiliation/identification. This growing strength can determine the outcome of elections. Hence it is important for candidates to understand the issues and solutions the AAPI electorate cares about.

Conclusion: A Vision for Political Inclusion and Equality

As AAPI communities continue to grow, the AAPI infrastructure continues to mature, and more AAPIs enter all levels of the political process, there is optimism for great progress going into the future, and the surge in AAPI political power is certain and undeniable. Current trends and future projections make this clear—the influence of AAPIs on American civic life is only beginning to thrive.

Yet it is also critical that the work of building political infrastructure, engaging AAPI voters, and developing a pipeline of future leaders is at the core of this thriving AAPI future. Without consistent and sustainable engagement, we lose control of determining the future for AAPI communities. In order to shut down demeaning rhetoric, deconstruct stereotypes, and speak for AAPIs instead of others speaking over AAPIs, AAPIs must continue to develop and grow the infrastructure that made the tremendous growth of the last few decades possible. AAPIs must continue to invest the resources—financial and in-kind—that enable this type of growth to continue.

Today, it is rightfully possible to imagine a future when issues facing AAPIs take political priority, when AAPI voters are the most sought-after vote, and when the number of AAPIs at all levels of elected or appointed office reaches and/or exceeds parity. That future is our vision for political equality for 2040 and beyond.

Notes

1. Language access provisions, particularly through Section 203 of the Voting Rights Act, are key in ensuring LEP AAPIs have access to the ballot. Language access provisions and initiatives, even outside of jurisdictions covered by Section 203, continue to help enfranchise communities. Section 203 of the Voting Rights Act mandates language assistance in political subdivisions and jurisdictions with significant language minority populations. The law covers areas where there are more than ten thousand or more than 5 percent of total voting age citizens in a political subdivision who are members of a single minority language group and are LEP. Drawn from U.S. Census data, Section 203 jurisdictions may change every decade based on population changes, with the most recent additions to Section 203 coverage in 2011. Political subdivisions are typically based on county, but can also be applied to municipalities and townships. Jurisdictions in ten states are currently covered under Section 203 for Asian languages, and they include ethnic groups such as Asian Indian, Bangladeshi, Cambodian, Chinese, Filipino, Japanese, Korean, Thai, and Vietnamese.

2. Comments such as those from former governor Jeb Bush, calling Asians "anchor babies," is one example of divisive tactics that denigrate AAPIs in the United States.

3. The time gap from 1984 to 1995 was due to the *National Asian Pacific American Political Almanac* not being bi-annually produced during this interval.

4. The other states with AAEOs (number in parenthesis) were Colorado (2), Idaho (1), Maryland (1), Utah (3), Pennsylvania (1), Nebraska (1), Oregon (3), and Washington (9).

5. According to the 2010 Census, Asian Americans (alone or in combination) represented the following percentages in these states: California (14.9), Hawaii (57.4), Washington (9), Maryland (6.4), Illinois (5.2), Virginia (6.5), and Texas (4.4).

6. Political incorporation refers to "the extent to which group interests are effectively represented in policy-making" in U.S. cities (see Browning, Marshall, and Tabb, 2003, 11).

References

Asian and Pacific Islander American Vote and Asian Americans Advancing Justice—AAJC. 2014. *APIAVote and Asian Americans Advancing Justice I AAJC 2014 Voter Survey*. Washington, DC: Asian and Pacific Islander American Vote and Asian Americans Advancing Justice—AAJC.

Browning, Rufus P., Marshall, Dale Rogers, and David H. Tabb, eds. 2003. *Racial Politics in American Cities*, 3rd ed. New York: Longman Press.

File, Thom, and Camille Ryan. 2014. "Computer and Internet Use in the United States: 2013." *American Community Survey Reports.* Washington, DC: U.S. Census Bureau.

Kwoh, Stewart, and Mindy Hui. 1993. "Empowering Our Communities: Political Policy." Pp. 189–97 in *The State of Asian Pacific America: Policy Issues to the Year 2020.* Los Angeles: LEAP Asian Pacific American Public Policy Institute and UCLA Asian American Studies Center.

Lai, James S. 2011. *Asian American Political Action: Suburban Transformations.* Boulder, CO: Lynne Rienner Publishers.

———. 2009. "A New Gateway: Asian American Political Power in the 21st Century." *Amerasia Journal* 35(3): 133–38.

Lien, Pei-te. *The Making of Asian America through Political Participation.* Philadelphia: Temple University Press, 2001.

Nakanishi, Don T., and James S. Lai, eds. 1978–2014. *National Asian Pacific American Political Almanac.* Editions 1–15. Los Angeles: UCLA Asian American Studies Center Press.

National Association of Latino Elected Officials Education Fund. 2015. *National Directory of Latino Elected Officials.* Los Angeles: National Association of Latino Elected Officials Education Fund.

Ong, Jonathan, Ong, Paul, and Elena Ong. 2016. "The Future of Asian America in 2040." *AAPI Nexus Journal: Policy, Practice, and Community* 14(1): 14–29.

Ong, Paul, and Albert Lee. 2010. "Asian Americans and Redistricting: Empowering through Electoral Boundaries." *AAPI Nexus Journal* 8(2): 87–114.

Ong, Paul, and Don T. Nakanishi. 1996. "Becoming Citizens, Becoming Voters: The Naturalization and Political Participation of Asian Pacific Immigrants." Pp. 275–305 in Ronald Lee and Bill Ong Hing, eds. *Reframing the Immigration Debate.* Los Angeles: LEAP Asian Pacific American Public Policy Institute and UCLA Asian American Studies Center.

Ong, Paul and Elena Ong. 2015. "The Future of Asian America in 2040: Asian American Electorate to Double." UCLA Center for the Study of Inequality and Asian Pacific American Institute for Congressional Studies. http://luskin.ucla.edu/sites/default/files/AA2040_report.pdf (accessed April 14, 2016).

Ong, Paul, De La Cruz-Viesca, Melany, and Don Nakanishi. 2008. "Awakening the New 'Sleeping Giant'? Asian American Political Engagement." *AAPI Nexus Journal* 6(1): 1–10.

Ramakrishnan, S. Karthick. 2005. *Democracy in Immigrant America: Changing Demographics and Political Participation.* Palo Alto: Stanford University Press.

Ramakrishnan, Karthick, and Farah Ahmad. 2014. *State of Asian Americans and Pacific Islanders.* Washington, DC: Center for American Progress.

Rosenblum, Marc R., and Ariel G. Ruiz Soto. 2015. "An Analysis of Unauthorized Immigrants in the United States by Country and Region of Birth." Washington, DC: Migration Policy Institute.

San Diego County Registrar of Voters. 2013. "Case Study: 2010 Governor's Race." San Diego, CA: Registrar of Voters.

Waters, Mary C., and Marisa Gerstein Pineau, eds. 2015. *The Integration of Im-*

migrants into American Society. Washington, DC: National Academies Press.

Wong, Janelle S. 2006. *Democracy's Promise: Immigrants and American Civic Institutions*. Ann Arbor: University of Michigan Press.

Wong, Janelle, S. Karthick Ramakrishnan, Taeku Lee, and Jane Junn. *Asian American Political Participation: Emerging Constituents and Their Political Identities*. New York: Russell Sage Foundation, 2011.

CHRISTINE CHEN, the founding executive director of Asian and Pacific Islander American Vote from 2006 to 2008, returned to APIAVote in 2011 to serve as its current Executive Director. During her tenure, she strengthened and expanded APIAVote's partners into twenty-two states. APIAVote's research and polling of Asian American voters and its regional trainings and field programs have strengthened the local grassroots programs in reaching and mobilizing AAPI voters. Through these efforts, APIAVote has played a key role in elevating the AAPI electorate to an unprecedented national level in recent years. Formerly, she served as executive director of Organization of Chinese Americans—National from 2001 to 2005.

KARTHICK RAMAKRISHNAN is Professor of Public Policy and Political Science at the University of California, Riverside, where he also serves as Associate Dean of the School of Public Policy. He is also an Adjunct Fellow at Public Policy Institute of California. Ramakrishnan directs the National Asian American Survey and is founder of AAPIdata.com, which seeks to make policy-relevant data on AAPIs more accessible to a variety of audiences. He has written several books and articles on Asian Americans and immigrants more generally, and these can be found on his website (http://karthick.com).

JAMES S. LAI is an Associate Professor who holds a joint appointment with the Ethnic Studies Program and the Department of Political Science at Santa Clara University. Dr. Lai served as the Director of the Ethnic Studies Program from 2008 to 2014. His teaching and research interests and specialties include U.S. racial and ethnic politics, U.S. immigration, Asian American politics, urban politics, community studies, and California state and local politics. Since 1992, Dr. Lai has served as the Associate Editor of the bi-annual publication *National Asian Pacific American Political Almanac*, the nation's most comprehensive political guide on Asian American politics (UCLA Asian American Studies Press).

ALTON WANG is the Communications and Development Associate at Asian and Pacific Islander American Vote, where he coordinates its communications and media strategy, youth engagement, and organizational development. Originally from the San Gabriel Valley outside Los Angeles, he studied at Wesleyan University in Connecticut where he spearheaded a push for Asian American studies on Wesleyan's campus, as well as teaching a for-credit course on Asian American history. Wang has experience in online organizing, community outreach, as well as coalition building. He continues to have an active presence advocating for issues affecting AAPIs, including blogging online.